The Institute of B
Studies in Biolog

D1630412

The Optical Microscope
in Biology

Savile Bradbury

M.A., D.Phil., Dipl. R.M.S.

University Lecturer in Human Anatomy
and
Fellow of Pembroke College, Oxford

Edward Arnold

© Savile Bradbury 1976

First published 1976
by Edward Arnold (Publishers) Limited,
25 Hill Street, London W1X 8LL

Boards edition ISBN: 0 7131 2532 2
Paper edition ISBN: 0 7131 2533 0

All Rights Reserved. No part of this publication
may be reproduced, stored in a retrieval system,
or transmitted in any form or by any means, electronic,
mechanical, photocopying, recording or otherwise, without
the prior permission of Edward Arnold (Publishers) Limited.

Printed in Great Britain by
The Camelot Press Ltd., Southampton

General Preface to the Series

It is no longer possible for one textbook to cover the whole field of Biology and to remain sufficiently up to date. At the same time teachers and students at school, college or university need to keep abreast of recent trends and know where the most significant developments are taking place.

To meet the need for this progressive approach the Institute of Biology has for some years sponsored this series of booklets dealing with subjects specially selected by a panel of editors. The enthusiastic acceptance of the series by teachers and students at school, college and university shows the usefulness of the books in providing a clear and up-to-date coverage of topics, particularly in areas of research and changing views.

Among features of the series are the attention given to methods, the inclusion of a selected list of books for further reading and, wherever possible, suggestions for practical work.

Readers' comments will be welcomed by the author or the Education Office of the Institute.

1975   The Institute of Biology,
                               41 Queens Gate,
                               London, SW7 5HU.

Preface

The optical microscope has now been used for biological observations throughout the last three hundred years. During the greater part of this time the instrument has been used to provide morphological information on the minute structure of plants and animals, limited, however, by the ultimate resolution achievable with the conventional light microscope of 0.25 μm in the most favourable circumstances. Following the introduction of the electron microscope with its enhanced resolution, the view has therefore gained support that the future use of the optical microscope is now severely limited. It is possible to argue, however, that this is surely a fallacious opinion. The use of contrast-enhancing techniques allows the detailed structural changes of living cells to be studied, whilst fluorescent markers allow dynamic processes to be observed. More recently a whole new range of methods has been developed for using the optical microscope as a quantitative or analytical tool, either directly or in conjunction with automatic techniques for the acquisition and processing of information contained within the microscopical image.

The present book represents an attempt to introduce some of these new developments to students and other users of the optical microscope. It is hoped that the reader is left with the conclusion that the optical microscope still has a most important role in biological research.

Oxford, 1975   S. B.

Contents

Acknowledgements

Figure 1–5 is reproduced by courtesy of Wild Heerbrugg Ltd; Figs. 1–6
and 3–10 by courtesy of Vickers Instruments; Fig. 3–11 by courtesy of
Imanco Ltd., photograph by T. Reeve, A.I.I.P. I am grateful to Dr. A.
Ostberg for Fig. 2–11.

1 The Instrument

1.1 Introduction

Of the several senses of the vertebrate body, vision is perhaps the most important; for the human a great part of our conceptual world is built up from the pattern of nerve impulses from our eyes which reach our brains and are interpreted as representations of the environment around us.

From ancient times up to the end of the sixteenth century no optical devices were available to help inspect what lay either close at hand or at very great distances. Once it had been discovered that lenses could be used to assist the eye, spectacles, the telescope and the microscope were soon developed. In both telescope and microscope the apparent size of an object at the eye is increased and greater detail is then discernible in the final image. If a single lens is used to examine small objects we have a *simple microscope*, whilst if more than one lens is used to enlarge the image of the object, the arrangement is called a *compound microscope*.

The early compound microscopes were clumsy to use and crude in construction; they suffered from many optical aberrations and were useful only for examining the surfaces of objects. Nevertheless, even the low magnifications possible with these early instruments were sufficient to spark off tremendous interest and open up a whole new world for study. Hooke's *Micrographia* of 1665 detailed the structure of many common objects, including the cells in a slice of cork, the surface of leaves and small insects. Shortly afterwards Malpighi observed the circulation of the blood in the capillaries of the frog lung and illustrated the development of the chick embryo.

In the eighteenth century little technical progress in microscopy was made, but there was a great breakthrough in the following hundred years. Corrected lenses became available and it was discovered how to combine them without introducing errors into the optical system. Mechanical construction of microscopes was perfected, but above all, as a result of the work of Abbe in Germany, the formation of the image in the microscope was explained. By 1890 it was clear that the maximum resolution (i.e. the ability to see fine detail clearly) theoretically possible with an optical microscope had been attained. At the same time, tremendous innovations had been made in the methods for preparing specimens for examination with the microscope; it was possible to cut tissues into thin slices for study and to impart vivid colour contrasts to their various parts by the use of the new synthetic aniline dyes. Such methods led to the use of the microscope in many fresh fields such as pathology, cytology and bacteriology.

Modern developments in microscopy have been very diverse. The search for ever-increasing resolution has led to the development of the electron microscope (see the companion volume in this series by A. V. Grimstone). This new tool has already proved of tremendous value by extending the range of our observations. It must not, however, be thought that the electron microscope has rendered the optical microscope obsolete! The tendency now is to consider the optical microscope not only as a means of seeing more structural detail, but also as an instrument for examining events in living tissues and as an analytical tool.

1.2   Resolution and magnification

Resolution is a measure of the ability to recognize two individual but closely-spaced points as separate, i.e. the visualization of fine detail. It is essential to differentiate between the resolution of a system and the nominal 'resolving power' of the system. This latter is a property of any optical instrument and its recording system, whether it be the eye, a photographic plate or a television camera. The actual resolution of any system may be equal to the nominal resolving power or less than it, due to many variables such as the presence of aberrations, the intensity of illumination and contrast levels.

The magnification of the microscope may be defined as the ratio of the apparent size of the image of an object to the actual size of the object itself. In practice this is obtained by multiplying the primary magnification of the objective lens (M_o) by that of the eyepiece (M_e); the expression for total magnification (M_T) of any microscope system may be then written:

$$M_T = M_o \times M_e$$

The human eye is a relatively poor performer in terms of resolving power, estimates of which vary according to the method of measurement used. Other factors such as the image contrast and the intensity of illumination must also be considered when discussing the resolution of the eye. An average value for this may be taken as 0.1 mm or one minute of arc at the nearest distance of distinct vision (conventionally 250 mm for a normal eye). Figure 1-1 shows two half-tone screens, each formed of a series of dots separated by differing distances. On the left-hand side of the figure the separation is well above the resolving power of most unaided eyes and the dots of the screen can be seen easily; on the right, however, where the spacing is much closer, only a blur is apparent. With the aid of a magnifying glass, which increases the apparent angle subtended by the object at the eye, the dots of the fine screen too can be resolved as separate entities.

It thus follows that even if detail is resolved by a microscope it will not be apparent in the final image unless the detail has a diameter greater than about 0.1 mm. It is partly due to this limitation of the eye itself that a minimum magnification is desirable in any microscope system.

Fig. 1–1   Two areas of uniform grey tint, reproduced through a half-tone screen. On the left there are sixty-five dots/inch and they are clearly resolved by the naked eye. On the right, where there are one hundred and thirty-three dots/inch, the naked eye cannot perceive the structure but examination with a magnifying glass shows them to be present.

Theoretical considerations suggest that this minimum magnification should be about two hundred times the numerical aperture (see below, p. 5) of the object lens in use. It is, of course, possible to increase the total magnification of a microscope by increasing the initial power of the objective lens or the eyepiece, or both. If there is detail in the image produced by the objective lens, then more information may well be gained in this way, as the detail in the final image will then be imaged at a size well above the limit imposed by the resolving power of the observer's eye. There is a limit, however, to this increase of magnification above which further enlargement does not serve to bring out any more detail, but only to increase in size that which was already apparent. Above this point (which can be shown to be about one thousand times the numerical aperture of the objective) any further increase leads to what is termed 'empty magnification'. A crude analogy is given by a photograph in a newspaper. The photograph is reproduced by means of a half-tone screen which breaks up the image into a series of dots. With the naked eye these dots are just at or below the resolution limit of the eye and they do not prevent us seeing the details of the picture itself. If we now examine the picture with a strong magnifier in the hope of seeing further detail then we are usually disappointed; the half-tone screen dots become clearly visible and impair our perception of the picture itself.

The chief limit to the resolution of the optical microscope is not, as might be supposed, the aberrations of the lenses but the fact that light may be considered to be of a wave nature. Because of this an edge or a hole in an opaque object cannot be imaged clearly due to the spreading of the light waves as a result of the phenomenon of diffraction. A hole in an opaque film, for example, is imaged not as a single bright spot but as a series of dark and light rings of progressively increasing diameter surrounding the central spot of light. This appearance (Fig. 1–2a) is known as the Airy disc. When two separate holes very close together are imaged the diffraction patterns overlap (Fig. 1–2c), the image appearance becomes confused and it is often difficult to say whether in fact we are looking at the image of one or of more than one hole. There must always be some degree of subjective judgement of the point at which resolution may be said to occur. If the two points are considered to be self-luminous

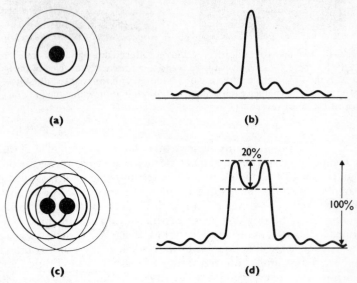

(a)   (b)

(c)   (d)

Fig. 1–2   (a) The appearance of the Airy disc. The central bright spot of light is surrounded by diffraction rings. (b) Densitometer tracing across the Airy disc in (a). (c) Two Airy discs produced by two points close together. (d) Densitometer tracing across the Airy disc in (c). The intensity drop between the two maxima is about 20% and the two points would just be resolved.

(or the two holes are illuminated by incoherent light) then the observed intensity of the light in the image is equal to the sum of that associated with each object in the object plane considered separately. In the case we are considering, namely two holes in an opaque film lying very close together, the resultant intensities in the image plane obtained by traversing a densitometer over the image may be represented as in Fig. 1–2d. If the central decrease in intensity is about 20% of the total then the convention is to say that the two points would be just resolved as separate. This criterion, originally proposed by Lord Rayleigh for the resolution of spectroscopic images, is fulfilled if the central maximum of one pattern just coincides with the first minimum of the other. It is possible to calculate the separation (d_{min}) of points in the object which will just satisfy this criterion. Theoretical considerations show that

$$d_{min} = \frac{0.61\,\lambda}{n \cdot \sin \alpha}$$

where λ is the wavelength of the illuminating light, n is the refractive index of the medium around the object and α is half the acceptance angle of the lens. (The acceptance angle of a lens is the angle subtended by the apex of the solid cone of light rays diverging from an object near the focus of the lens. This light can enter the lens to form the image and is represented by the angle AOB in Fig. 1–8a.) For the derivation of this expression, the works quoted in the bibliography may be consulted. Abbe introduced the term 'numerical aperture' (N.A.) for the term $n \cdot \sin \alpha$ in the above equation. This concept allows lenses to be compared in terms of their theoretical maximum possible resolution and is also a rough measure of the light-gathering ability of the lens.

Abbe was the first microscopist to realize the importance of the light diffracted by the specimen in the formation of the image of an object. This diffracted light provides information about the structure of the specimen; the more complete this information (i.e. the more diffracted light accepted by the lens), then the closer the resemblance between the amplitude distribution of the light in the image plane and that in the object plane, i.e. the better the resultant image will be and the closer its resemblance to the object. From Abbe's work it is apparent that for any detail to be imaged by the microscope objective at least one diffraction maximum must enter the lens. As the object detail becomes finer, the diffraction maxima produced by the object become more widely spaced (Fig. 1–3). For any given lens, a spacing of object detail will be reached

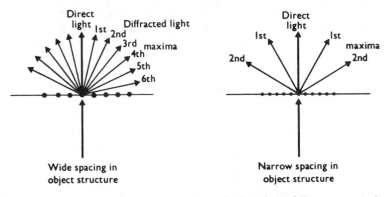

Fig. 1–3   The diffraction maxima produced when light falls on a periodic specimen. The closer the periodicity, the wider the spacing of the diffraction maxima.

where none of the diffraction maxima fall within the acceptance angle of the lens and at this point no detail can be resolved by that lens. In order to resolve finer detail we can either increase the numerical aperture of the lens or reduce the wavelength of the illuminating light. In practice it is difficult to increase the numerical aperture above 1.4, so that only the latter course is practicable. As the illumination we use must (a) interact with the specimen and (b) be capable of being brought to a focus by lenses, we are limited in our choice of a shorter wavelength radiation. Of the various possible alternatives, X-rays will satisfy the first but not the second criterion, γ-rays satisfy neither criterion; beams of negatively-charged electrons are suitable and may be used, however, since they are scattered by the specimen and can be focused by electrostatic or electromagnetic lenses. The use of electron beams for examining objects forms the basis of the increased resolution shown by the electron microscope.

In the above discussion both the lens system and the object have been considered as perfect; in practice, however, the contrast of the image and the aberrations of the lens system play a large part in determining how closely the resolution of the system approaches the theoretical maximum. Using the highest quality of lenses, blue-green light and a thin, contrasty object, the maximum resolution of the conventional optical microscope is generally about 0.25 μm. In certain types of microscopy (e.g. dark-ground (see section 2.2) when the image contrast is very high), it is possible to detect the *presence* of considerably smaller particles, but under these conditions it is not possible to say anything about the actual structure of such particles.

1.3   Types of microscope

For many years the best observations were made with a single uncorrected lens of short focal length. Such simple microscopes were extensively used up to the beginning of the nineteenth century. Leeuwenhoek, who ground all his own lenses, worked exclusively with simple microscopes (Fig. 1–4a) and by their aid described and drew protozoa, bacteria and much of the histological detail of higher organisms. In the nineteenth century Robert Brown used a simple microscope to discover the nucleus of the plant cell and the irregular motion of small suspended particles in a fluid. Simple microscopes are still used today for the low magnifications required in preparative work and some branches of biology. The simple microscope provides an image which is magnified, erect and virtual (Fig. 1–4b). The image is remarkably free from chromatic and spherical aberrations, but unless the lens is rendered aspherical there is often a pronounced curvature of the field. These microscopes are hard to use, as they have to be brought very close to the eye; they have only a very limited field of view and it is often difficult to mount and illuminate the specimen adequately.

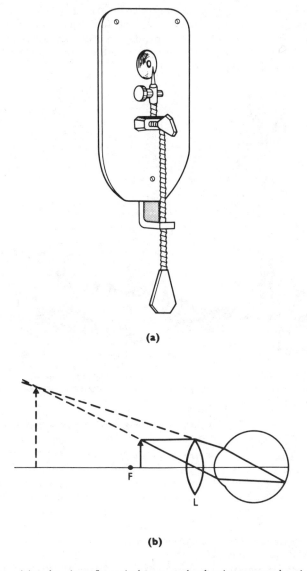

(a)

(b)

Fig. 1–4 (a) A drawing of a typical Leeuwenhoek microscope, showing the pin which carries the object to be examined and the screw threads which move its position. The plate of the instrument body was about $1\frac{1}{2}''$ long. (b) Image formation in the simple microscope. The object is placed just inside the focal point F of the lens, L, in order to provide a final image which is virtual, erect and magnified.

For the majority of low power microscopy today (i.e. up to a magnification of ×100) the stereoscopic binocular microscope would be used (Fig. 1–5). These instruments produce a true stereoscopic image which is erect and the right-way round, so they are especially suitable for dissecting and operating.

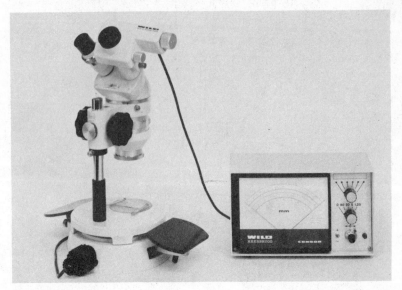

Fig. 1–5 A modern stereoscopic binocular microscope used for dissection purposes; this instrument is fitted with an electronic length measuring attachment (see section 3.4).

Early stereo binoculars were of the Greenhough type where each eye viewed the object through a separate inclined microscope tube mounted together so that the fields of view were coincident. Recently the tendency has been towards the use of the 'split-field objective' type where one large objective is used, the light from which is divided by beam splitters between the two eyepiece tubes. Often an elaborate auxiliary lens system for changing the magnifications, or even a continuously-variable zoom lens system, is added to increase the versatility of the instrument. Stereo microscopes have a very long working distance and are invaluable in the modern biology laboratory.

The standard compound microscope (Fig. 1–6) uses an objective lens to form the magnified primary image which is then viewed and further magnified with the eyepiece or ocular. The final image is magnified and virtual but, in contrast to the simple microscope, it is also inverted. Under certain circumstances, however, the compound microscope can be arranged to produce a real image for projection, drawing or photography. Compound microscopes vary in design from the very straightforward student instrument to large, most elaborate research stands. The optical system of objective and eyepiece is fitted on to a short body tube which is usually carried on a limb which forms the main part of the instrument and is nowadays a very solid component. The limb carries the specimen support stage mounted at right angles to the optical axis whilst the illuminating equipment (the substage condenser, its associated centring and focusing devices and often a built-in lamp) is mounted beneath the specimen stage. If a low-voltage lamp is not built into the microscope a mirror mounted in gimbals is fitted below the substage condenser in order to allow an external light source to be used.

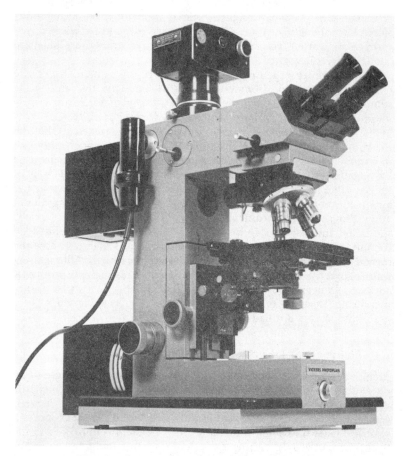

Fig. 1–6 A large modern compound microscope, with a binocular eyepiece head, nosepiece carrying several objectives and built-in illumination.

All microscopes are fitted with some means of focusing the image; either the tube carrying the objective and eyepiece may be moved up and down relative to the specimen stage by means of rackwork, or more commonly today, the stage is moved relative to the objective and eyepiece which are firmly attached to the limb. This latter arrangement has several practical advantages, especially with regard to stability. Often slide holders (so-called 'mechanical stages') are fitted to the specimen stage to enable the slide carrying the object to be moved by means of a rackwork mechanism; this allows easy searching of fields under high power lenses and the accurate positioning of objects in the field of view. Mechanical stages are a great convenience in microscopy. Most modern instruments now have the different powers of objective lens carried on a circular disc of metal—the revolving nosepiece—fitted at the lower end of the body tube. A revolving nosepiece allows the correct lens to be selected very quickly. In earlier years separate lens mounts known as 'objective changers' were in vogue.

With the more expensive and elaborate research microscopes, the tendency is to provide a binocular head. This presents the same image simultaneously to each eye through an arrangement of prisms and greatly minimizes fatigue when using the microscope for long periods.

Microscopes intended for biological use are constructed so that the image is produced by light transmitted through the specimen, although in recent years there has been some tendency to revert to the practice used by metallurgists and illuminate the specimen from above. This is of special value in some types of fluorescence microscopy (see section 2.4) and in a technique used for visualizing and estimating the silver grains in autoradiographs by measuring the light which they reflect. Various specialized microscope stands are used in biological work. One intended for the study of cultured cells by phase-contrast is inverted; here the optical imaging system is located beneath the stage with the 'illuminating train' above. Most of the large stands supplied for research purposes now contain an integral 35 mm film or plate camera, together with exposure measuring devices, to allow observations to be recorded photographically as they are made.

1.4   Illumination of the object

In the early days of microscopy, light was provided by daylight or by candles; in the nineteenth century, oil lamps were used. Often the illuminating system was arranged so that the light rays were concentrated on to the object from above, by means of a simple bull's-eye lens or even a spherical glass flask filled with brine. Such a system is illustrated in the frontispiece of Hooke's *Micrographia*. Later, when interest had moved to the study of objects by transmitted light, the same light sources were used but now the light rays were reflected from a mirror below the specimen stage into the optical axis of the microscope. Often a simple plano-convex lens concentrated the light and so acted as a rudimentary substage condenser.

A similar system is often used today, substituting an electric bulb for the oil lamp; such an arrangement of extrinsic illumination allows large and specialized light sources (requiring bulky lamphouses and special collector lenses) to be used if required. Many microscope stands, however, now incorporate a small light source together with the necessary collecting lenses, into the base of the microscope itself. These may be termed 'intrinsic' or built-in illumination systems (see Fig. 1–6). Built-in illumination minimizes the risk of misalignment of the light source and has proved a great convenience for routine work. It is usual in these systems for the path of the light rays to be turned into the optic axis of the instrument by a prism and hence no mirror is fitted. An iris diaphragm is always fitted in such a position that it can be imaged in the plane of the specimen and so act as a field stop, limiting the actual area of the specimen which is illuminated and hence helping to increase image contrast by reducing 'glare'.

The low voltage bulbs used in microscopy have specially designed filaments in which the coils of filament are bunched tightly together and lie side by side to form an extended or 'solid' source. The collector lens system can then produce a sufficiently large image to fill the whole aperture of the condenser, a necessary requirement for satisfactory high resolution microscopy. Tungsten filament lamps can give a very intense light which can easily be regulated (at the expense of some change in its colour temperature) by a variable resistance in the transformer circuit.

Recently quartz halogen lamps have come into use in microscopy. In these bulbs iodine or bromine vapour is included in the lamp to prevent blackening of the envelope by a deposit of tungsten sublimed from the filament. Such lamps have a high light output and a high colour temperature which makes them especially valuable for photo-micrography. Their high running temperature, however, means that they must have a large well-ventilated housing if they are to operate satisfactorily.

Many specialized light sources are now available, and it is not possible to deal with all of them here. High pressure mercury arcs, in particular, are now much used. These are excellent for providing monochromatic light, especially green at 546 nm; with suitable filters, the 365 nm line of the mercury arc can be isolated as a source of exciting radiation for fluorescence microscopy (see section 2.4). The xenon high pressure arc is used in colour photomicrography because of its great intensity and high colour temperature (6000K) which allows the use of daylight colour film without any further colour filtration.

Whatever type of illumination is used it is necessary for the light to be concentrated on to the specimen by means of the substage condenser.

Another important function of the condenser is to provide a light cone of suitable numerical aperture to match that of the objective. This control is performed by the iris diaphragm of the condenser. Special condensers are also used to achieve certain types of illumination, e.g. annular for both dark-ground microscopy and for phase-contrast.

For use with very low-power objectives a simple uncorrected plano-convex lens will serve as a suitable condenser. Routinely, however, the most commonly used system is that designed by Abbe; this has two lenses of crown glass arranged as shown in Fig. 1–7a. There are no chromatic corrections and the system also suffers badly from spherical aberration which often makes it impossible to illuminate the field evenly and may

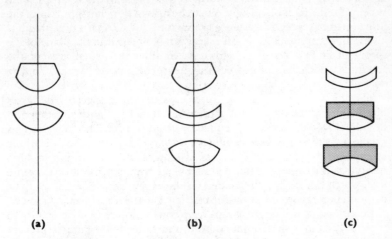

(a)   (b)   (c)

Fig. 1–7   Optical components of various microscope condensers seen in diagrammatic section. (a) Abbe type: uncorrected; (b) aplanatic type; (c) oil immersion achromatic type. The tinted areas indicate lenses made of flint glass (as opposed to crown glass) used for colour correction.

introduce strong glare, thus reducing the contrast of the final image. Although an Abbe condenser *may* be used with the highest powers of the microscope, a much better result is obtained by substituting a more elaborate condenser such as the aplanatic system (Fig. 1–7b). Aplanatic condensers are corrected to eliminate most of the spherical aberration and field curvature but they still suffer from chromatic aberration. For the very highest quality microscopy (e.g. when the condenser must provide a cone of light which will fill the whole aperture of a lens of N.A. 1.4) then the achromatic type of condenser (Fig. 1–7c) is required; here, in addition to spherical corrections, full chromatic corrections are also provided. Such condensers are operated with their upper lenses in oil immersion contact with the underside of the slide.

All condensers should be adjusted in use so that the object plane lies at their focus, i.e. at the apex of the illuminating cone of light. The condenser iris diaphragm is then set to give a cone of light which fills two-thirds to three-quarters of the aperture of the objective in use. Whatever type of condenser is in use it will be adjusted so that the illumination conforms to the condition known as either 'source-focus' or Köhler.

In the former (sometimes called 'Nelsonian' or 'critical' illumination) the condenser is arranged to project a focused image of the light source into the plane of the object. With an extended homogeneous light source such as an illuminated ground-glass screen or an opal bulb this system is perfectly adequate and serves for a large proportion of routine visual observations with the microscope. If small, intense inhomogeneous light sources are used (as in research microscopes intended for photography or for use with phase-contrast), then Köhler illumination is advisable. In this system the lamp housing has its own condenser which serves to focus an enlarged image of the lamp filament into the front focal plane of the microscope condenser. The microscope condenser then, in turn, focuses the image of the lamp condenser (which appears as an homogeneous secondary light source) into the object plane. This results in the final field of view appearing evenly illuminated. As there is an image of the light source in the front focal plane of the condenser, parallel light beams will emerge at all angles from the top of the condenser, and will be collected and focused by the microscope objective to form another image of the lamp filament in the back focal plane of the objective. This latter image must be large enough to fill the working aperture of the objective with light, hence the desirability of large extended filaments in the low voltage lamps used in Köhler illumination. With both types of illumination an iris diaphragm fitted to the lamp housing serves to limit the area of the field of view which is illuminated and thus control glare which would otherwise degrade the quality of the final image.

1.5   The microscope objective

The microscope objective is perhaps the most important component of the microscope system, providing as it does both the primary image with its resolved fine detail and much of the magnification of the microscope system. Several basic types of objective are in current use. Each type is available in a range of focal lengths with varying initial magnifications and numerical apertures (see Table 1).

The numerical aperture of a microscope objective is a number which represents the product of the sine of α (half the acceptance angle of the lens) and the refractive index of the medium in which the lens is working (Fig. 1–8a). As this is often air (with a refractive index of 1.0) the expression for the N.A. then becomes equal to sin α; since the maximum possible value of α is 90°, sin α will thus be equal to 1.0 and this is therefore the maximum theoretical numerical aperture attainable by a dry lens. In practice the upper limit is about 0.95 (Fig. 1–8b). With the higher power lenses and those (such as planapochromats) of exceptional quality, oil of refractive index equal to that of glass is usually placed between the object and the front lens of the objective. This renders the medium in which the light rays travel optically homogeneous and eliminates reflection from the under surface of the coverslip of those light rays which exceed the critical angle for glass to air. As there is no refraction of light rays on

Table 1   Different types of microscope objective lenses

Type of objective	Approx. Focal length (mm)	Approx. N.A.	Approx. Initial magnifications
Achromat	25	0.18	× 6
(dry)	16	0.22	× 10
	4	0.60	× 40
Achromat			
(oil immersion)	2	1.25	× 100
Fluorite			
(dry)	4	0.75	× 40
(oil immersion)	2	1.30	× 100
Planapochromatic			
(dry)	16	0.30	× 10
(oil immersion)	4	1.00	× 40
(oil immersion)	2	1.30	× 100
Apochromatic			
(oil immersion)	2	1.40	× 90

leaving the coverslip or on entering the front element of the objective lens, the acceptance angle is increased greatly compared to that of a dry lens and hence the numerical aperture of the system may be increased to a maximum value of about 1.4 (Fig. 1–8c). Such high-aperture lenses allow the widely separated first-order diffraction maxima from very fine periodicities to enter the image-forming system and thus allow the resolution of very fine detail. For further details of the influence of numerical aperture on resolution and of the methods of measurement of numerical aperture, the standard reference works listed in the bibliography may be consulted.

The introduction of highly corrected immersion lenses of high N.A., i.e. from 1.0 up to 1.4, proved to be a turning-point in biological microscopy, as it was only with such lenses that the finer details of cellular structure, of chromosomes and of bacteria became easily visible.

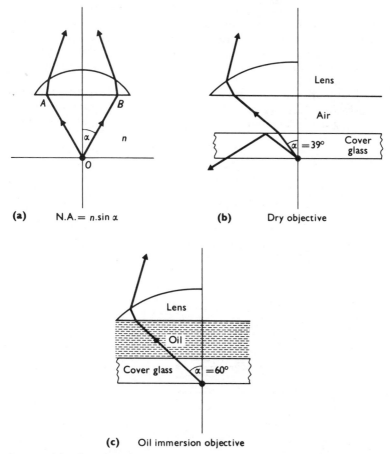

(a)   N.A.= $n.\sin \alpha$ **(b)**   Dry objective

(c)   Oil immersion objective

Fig. 1–8   (a) A diagram to represent the concept of numerical aperture (N.A.). n is the refractive index of the medium (usually air) between the object O and the lens, α is half the angle of acceptance AOB. (b) Path of light rays in a dry objective of N.A. 0.95. The maximum value of α is 39° due to refraction at the air/cover glass interface. Rays with a greater obliquity are totally reflected at the surface of the cover glass. (c) Path of light rays in an oil immersion objective of N.A. 1.3. The value of α is now increased to 60° since there is now no air/glass interface refraction.

Microscope objectives are all corrected to a greater or a lesser degree for the principal aberrations which affect lenses (spherical, chromatic, astigmatism, curvature of field and coma). The necessity for achieving such corrections increases the number of optical elements involved in the construction of the lens, especially as the numerical aperture increases.

An achromatic doublet lens will suffice at very low numerical apertures (c. 0.1 and below) with their attendant low levels of initial magnification, whereas a flat-field oil immersion lens of the highest quality and a numerical aperture of 1.4, may contain as many as fourteen separate lenses, either mounted singly or combined as doublets or triplets (Fig. 1–9).

The objectives most commonly used for routine microscopy are known as *achromats*; these lenses have their chromatic aberration corrected by bringing the red and blue rays to a common focus. This leaves a faint

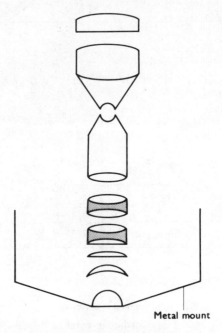

Metal mount

Fig. 1–9   A diagrammatic section of an oil immersion planapochromatic lens of high aperture. Note the large number of lens elements, some of complex shapes. The supporting lens mounts are not illustrated.

residual colour (the secondary spectrum) of a pale apple-green which may be sometimes seen around the edge of objects which exhibit a great deal of contrast. Spherical aberration in achromats is corrected for a single wavelength, usually chosen in the yellow-green part of the spectrum; these lenses, therefore, perform best when used with a green filter passing light of a wavelength around 550 nm. Achromats are easy to use as they have fairly generous working distances, i.e. clearance between the front lens of the objective and the upper surface of the coverslip of the object slide. These lenses suffice for about 90% of all routine visual use of the microscope.

Semiapochromatic or *fluorite* objectives are better corrected for both spherical and chromatic aberrations and have higher numerical apertures than achromats of corresponding focal lengths. The fluorite lenses have, however, a shorter working distance than the corresponding achromats and they show what is termed 'chromatic difference of magnification' in the primary image. This means that the image is slightly different in size for the two extreme colours of the spectrum. In order to correct this, special 'compensating' eyepieces are used which introduce an equal but opposite error, so correcting the final image.

The highest quality of optical corrections are found in the apochromatic series of objectives. Apochromats have a virtually complete colour correction, and are corrected for spherical aberration at two wavelengths. Such high degrees of correction are obtained at the expense of their aberrations and apochromats show the chromatic difference of magnification mentioned above, together with a very pronounced curvature of field. In some of the older lenses of this type it is not uncommon to find that only the central area of the field appears sharp at a given focus setting, the peripheral areas appearing as a complete blur. This drawback renders some of the older apochromatic lenses unsuitable for modern work involving photographic recording of the image. With the advent of newer optical glasses and the use of computers in lens design, today's microscope objectives are now much improved in their corrections and the current trend is to provide a whole series of lenses of the highest quality of corrections, including flatness of field. Such lenses are available from several manufacturers and are known as 'flat-field' lenses or, according to the degree of their corrections, as plana-pochromats or planachromats. It is now customary deliberately to introduce chromatic difference of magnification into the cheaper achromatic lenses so that only one type of eyepiece will be required for any set of objective lenses.

Many special types of microscope objective lens are available. Some are equipped with built-in phase-plates so that they may be used to view unstained living material (see section 2.3); some are designed (for the examination of metal surfaces) to operate without a coverslip and with incident light. Yet others are constructed so that they are optically strain-free and hence may be used with polarized light. Long working distance objectives have been built to allow the performance of surgical operations on living cells in culture or to permit the examination of metal surfaces at elevated temperatures in a small furnace fitted on to the microscope stage. By far the greater part of biological microscopy, however, can be performed with relatively conventional microscope objectives.

1.6 The microscope eyepiece

The eyepiece serves several purposes, first and foremost among which is the further magnification of the detail present in the primary image produced by the objective, so that the final virtual image viewed by the eye has detail of such a size that it can be seen without difficulty. It is possible, however, to project a real image of the object; this is useful for drawing or photography.

In many modern eyepieces deliberate aberrations are introduced into the image. These aberrations are carefully calculated to correct for the residual optical aberrations present in the primary image produced by the objective and so the overall effect is to increase the quality of the final image.

The eyepiece also serves to introduce graticules, limiting diaphragms or pointers, into the plane of the primary image so that they appear in sharp focus at the same time as this image. This is of particular value for measurement, teaching purposes and especially for quantitative work (see section 3.4).

Eyepieces now in use may be divided into two main categories, the negative or Huyghenian type and the positive or Ramsden eyepiece (Fig. 1–10). The construction of both types can be seen from this diagram; each normally contains two plano-convex lenses (the field lens and the eye lens) together with a diaphragm which limits the field of view. In the Huyghenian eyepiece both lenses are mounted with their convex surfaces towards the objective and with the diaphragm mounted in the primary image plane between the lenses.

The Ramsden eyepiece, which tends to be used for higher powers and when graticules have to be superimposed on the field of view, has the convex surface of each lens facing inwards and the field diaphragm below

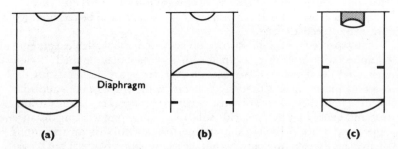

Fig. 1–10 Diagrammatic cross-sections of three types of eyepiece. (a) Negative or Huyghenian type; (b) positive or Ramsden type; (c) compensating Huyghenian type. In each eyepiece the diaphragm is located at the plane of the primary image produced by the objective.

the field lens. This means that the primary image plane is easily accessible in this type of eyepiece. Both types of eyepiece, although made from uncorrected lenses, are so designed that the spherical and chromatic aberrations of each lens cancel out.

Many eyepieces exist for special purposes; one in particular, the compensating eyepiece (Fig. 1–10), has already been mentioned. This type of eyepiece is designed to correct the lateral chromatic error of magnification inherent in objective lenses of high corrections and high apertures. With manufacturers now deliberately introducing such error into all of their objectives this type of eyepiece is rapidly becoming almost universal in use. Other eyepieces of especial interest to biologists are photomicrographic eyepieces which incorporate a 35 mm camera and viewing system, wide-field eyepieces for microanatomical work and scanning of large areas of specimen and some types of graticule-bearing eyepiece for stereological measurements.

Most of the eyepieces listed above can now be supplied with a construction which gives what is known as a 'high eye-point'. The eye-point (or Ramsden circle) is that point at which the cone of rays emerging from the eyepiece is brought to a focus. It should coincide with the pupil of the observer's eye otherwise the field of view becomes severely restricted. Spectacle wearers often use high eye-point eyepieces to allow them to examine the full visual field of the microscope whilst retaining the spectacles necessary to correct their refraction errors.

2 Contrast Methods in Optical Microscopy

2.1 Introduction

The majority of recent developments in optical microscope technology have been towards techniques which allow the instrument to be used as an analytical tool and so obtain numerical data from the specimens (see Chapter 3). It should not be thought, however, that this tendency has made the former role of the microscope completely obsolete; much valuable work can still be done using the instrument only for the morphological study of biological material, determining the shapes and inter-relationships of the cells which form the tissues and organs of the body. Such studies require that the microscope must not only resolve the fine detail in the structure but also form an image in which there is sufficient contrast for the structural differences to be appreciated. This contrast may be available in the object itself, if it is coloured, but in the majority of biological applications contrast has to be introduced either by staining the specimen or by optical means in the instrument itself.

When the compound microscope was first used to study biological material in the seventeenth century, it was used with low magnifications and almost entirely for the examination of surfaces—of leaves, moss capsules, pollen grains and so on. With such objects contrast is little or no problem; many are themselves coloured and the three-dimensional contouring is emphasized by the strong highlights and shadows which result from the incident light method of illumination which has to be used. Following improvements in the microscope itself in the nineteenth century and with the formulation of the cell theory the interests and studies of microscopists moved away from the study of surfaces towards an exploration of the cellular detail within the organs and tissues of which the organism was composed. In order to see anything of the internal structure it became necessary to study dead material which had been cut into thin slices. Such slices, or sections as they are called, allow excellent visualization of the internal detail but introduce other difficulties such as extrapolation from the two-dimensional image of such sections to an understanding of the actual structure in three-dimensions. The need for examination of thin slices of tissue led to the development of very complicated preparative techniques. When the thin (i.e. from $10-100\,\mu\text{m}$) sections had been produced it was found that if they were studied under the microscope without any further treatment they showed so little contrast that they were completely invisible; this had to be counteracted by staining the sections before they were examined. It has been said that the microtechnologist of the late nineteenth and early twentieth century had to be a cross between a dyer and a colour chemist, so complicated had some of these staining techniques become. Often three or four separate dyes of contrasting colours were used to reveal the detailed cellular morphology which was being described with the new high-quality apochromatic lenses of Abbe.

The techniques of sectioning and staining, followed by direct observation with the high-quality research microscope, still form the background for many research projects. Knowledge of normal detailed structure is essential before any attempt can be made to diagnose pathological changes and before any evaluation of the results of experimental procedures may be made. There has been a tendency in the last thirty years to move away from empirical methods of staining (where the different colours show only the difference between, say, muscle tissue and collagen fibres) towards techniques which reveal chemical differences in the composition of the cells and tissues as differences in staining reaction. Such techniques form the basis of the discipline called 'histochemistry'. It is now possible, for example, to colour specifically the deoxyribonucleic acid (DNA) in the nuclei and chromosomes. The technique, developed by Feulgen and Rossenbeck, uses the fact that hydrolysis with normal hydrochloric acid transforms the deoxy-sugars which are found in DNA into compounds containing exposed aldehyde groups. These, in their turn, are revealed by the use of Schiff's reagent (a colourless addition compound between the dye basic fuchsin and sulphurous acid) which imparts a strong magenta colour to compounds containing aldehyde groupings. This allows us to show up in high contrast the sites of DNA in the cell. In order to ensure specificity of the reaction it is essential to use suitable controls; for example, a second section must be passed through the Schiff's reagent having omitted the preliminary acid hydrolysis in order to ensure that no pre-existing aldehyde groups in the section were responsible for the staining.

Despite the tremendous value of staining techniques it is often necessary to examine material without their use. This may be for technical reasons or, more likely, because almost all the methods of staining involve killing the tissue and we may wish to examine the tissue whilst it is alive. Before the 1950's this was not an easy task, as only dark ground microscopy was available for this purpose. In the last two decades, however, the techniques of phase contrast and interference microscopy have superseded dark ground microscopy as a means for examining living cells or sections which have not been stained. At the same time the techniques of fluorescence microscopy have been developed; these now provided images of high contrast and for many biologists the use of immuno-fluorescence techniques has opened up the solutions to a whole range of exciting biological problems.

2.2   Dark ground microscopy

Dark ground microscopy is capable of providing images with a very high degree of contrast from either living or dead material which is unstained but which possesses marked discontinuities in the refractive index between itself and the surrounding mounting medium. The optical system is so arranged as to provide a brilliant image with reversed contrast, i.e. the image appears bright against a background which is completely dark (hence the name), whereas with most other methods the background tends to appear bright with a darker image of the object superimposed upon it. This reversal of contrast in the dark ground microscope does undoubtedly tend to increase the ability of the observer to detect the presence of fine structure, although of course, the actual resolution of the dark ground microscope is no better and, indeed, is sometimes not as good as that of the conventional instrument operated by bright-field transmitted light.

We have already seen (section 1.2 and Fig. 1–3) that in the formation of the microscope image both the direct light and the diffracted light originating from the object enter the objective lens and form an image with all its detail sharply resolved. If we now exclude all the direct light from participating in the image formation, either by preventing it from entering the lens or by blocking out the zero order maximum (Fig. 1–3) in the back focal plane of the objective, we still obtain an image full of detail *but* with the contrast reversed. Note that if we carry out the converse experiment, i.e. block out all the diffracted light, we do not get the reversal of contrast but instead we have complete loss of all the fine detail in the image.

In the practical realization of dark ground microscopy it is not feasible to occlude the direct light in the back focal plane of the objective by blanking out the zero order maximum. It is easier to achieve the same end by modifying the condenser system to produce a hollow cone of oblique light rays which illuminate the object. With low power objective lenses ($\times$10, $\times$25) this is done by inserting a central circular 'patch stop' into the front focal plane of the condenser. This produces the required hollow cone of light rays which, however, must have such an obliquity that the inner margin of the bundle of rays falls outside the acceptance angle of the objective lens (Fig. 2–1). It is obvious that the value of the acceptance angle will differ according to the numerical aperture and focal length of the objective in use, so that different sizes of patch stop will be required. When correctly made and adjusted, such simple patch stops will provide excellent dark ground. It is surprising that they are not provided as standard equipment on all biological microscopes, especially those intended for teaching. By the use of dark ground microscopy, details of the structure of aquatic organisms such as

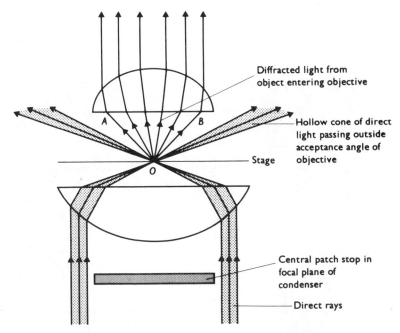

Diffracted light from object entering objective

Hollow cone of direct light passing outside acceptance angle of objective

Stage

Central patch stop in focal plane of condenser

Direct rays

Fig. 2–1 A diagram of the ray paths producing dark ground illumination by insertion of a patch stop below the condenser. Note that the obliquity of the ray bundles is such that no direct light falls within the acceptance angle (*AOB*) of the objective.

Rotifers, Protozoa such as *Stentor* and *Paramoecium*, small freshwater Coelenterates such as *Hydra*, and Crustacea such as *Daphnia* become vividly apparent (Fig. 2–2). Observation of the ciliary activity around the trumpet of *Stentor*, for example, is an unforgettable sight with dark ground illumination. For most freshwater biology this technique of microscopy surpasses all others in its simplicity and in the clarity of the results. Although the majority of microscopes are not provided with dark ground stops at the time of manufacture, these may easily be made at home (see bibliography).

Dark ground microscopy may also be applied to the higher powers of the instrument although problems arise when oil immersion lenses are used. If these have to be used with the dark ground technique it is necessary to make sure that they are worked for this purpose at an aperture smaller than that of the condenser (in order to ensure that all the direct light passes outside the objective); oil immersion objectives for dark ground microscopy are thus usually fitted with an iris diaphragm to reduce their numerical aperture to a suitable value. Patch stops cannot be used to produce dark ground effects with high power lenses. The illuminating cone of extreme obliquity required for these lenses is furnished instead by special reflecting condensers which operate in immersion contact with the underside of the microscope slide; this is so

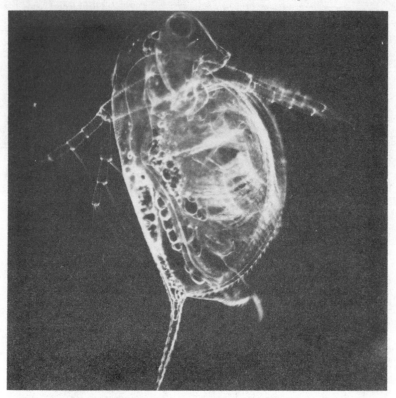

Fig. 2–2 Living *Daphnia* as seen by dark ground microscopy.

that the extremely oblique light rays are not reflected by the lower surface of the slide. Figure 2–3 shows in diagrammatic form two types of reflecting dark ground condenser. Of these, the paraboloid, now unfortunately almost unobtainable, was simple to use but was limited in the obliquity of the cone of rays which it could produce. This made it suitable for use with 'dry' lenses only. The second type, known as the 'cardioid', possesses both concave and convex mirror surfaces; it produces a cone of rays which are very oblique, so that it may be used with oil immersion lenses provided that their numerical aperture is slightly reduced. It is obvious that with any form of dark ground microscopy the object must be placed at the focus of the hollow cone of illumination.

This, in turn, means that accurate focusing of the condenser is essential together with accurate centration of the condenser to the optical axis of the instrument. As homogeneous immersion contact with the lower surface of the slide and the top lens of the condenser has to be maintained it is important that the slides must be of the correct thickness; slides which are too thick will not allow condenser focus to be obtained, whilst slides which are too thin will cause difficulty in maintaining the oil contact.

High power dark ground microscopy is not used extensively, although it has some value in haematology and in bacteriology. Indeed, high power dark ground is one of the best methods available for locating the presence in fresh blood samples of parasites such as Trypanosomes and of the Spirochaete *Treponema pallidum*, the causative agent of syphilis.

It should be stressed again that the resolution of the dark ground microscope does not improve upon that of the instrument using conventional illumination. The contrast, however, is very much enhanced

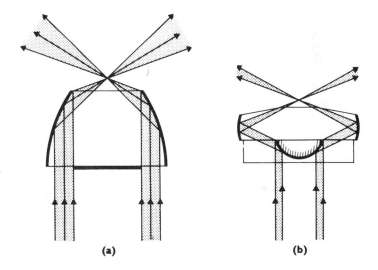

(a)   (b)

Fig. 2–3   The components of two types of reflecting dark ground condensers. (a) represents the 'paraboloid,' which has one reflecting surface; (b) is the 'cardioid' with one spherical convex and one cardioid reflecting surface.

in the thin, transparent objects with marked discontinuities of refractive index which form the most suitable subjects for this type of instrument. It must be remembered that the concept of resolution as such does not apply to very small particles when they are examined under dark ground, as with this technique their presence may be detected solely by their ability to scatter light. This was realized long before the invention of the electron microscope and was used by Siedentopf in his so-called 'ultra-microscope'. In this instrument a strong collimated beam of light illuminated the specimen from the side, i.e. at right angles to the optical axis of the microscope. Any small suspended particles in the liquid under study thus scattered light which was then detected by the microscope objective in the normal way. No information can be obtained about the shape of the particles but Siedentopf showed the presence in a liquid of suspended particles of only 4.0 nm diameter. Particles of this size are only 1/100th of the wave length of blue light. The lower limit is of course imposed by the intensity of the scattered light and by the contrast, i.e. the extent to which the background is lit up by the scattered light. The interest in this type of instrument was brief as it did not give any information on the shape of the particle, and methods of electron microscopy now allow direct visualization of such sub-microscopic particles.

At the end of the nineteenth century, microscopists were very interested in alternative methods of illuminating objects in order to increase the contrast of unstained material. One technique developed at that time by the English microscopist Julius Rheinberg (and now known by his name) was of a method of differential illumination very similar to that of the patch stop dark ground technique. Rheinberg illumination uses a two colour stop in which a central zone of a dark colour is surrounded by a peripheral zone of a lighter complementary colour. Operating on exactly the same principle as a patch stop, the background appears illuminated by the axial rays in the colour of the central zone stop, whilst objects in the field will scatter light from the oblique rays and so appear brightly illuminated in the lighter colour of the peripheral part of the disc. Rheinberg effects are aesthetically very pleasing but the technique does not yield any information which could not be obtained by conventional dark ground microscopy. One variant of the Rheinberg method, however, uses a stop composed of four quadrants of alternating complementary colours. When this is suitably orientated in the front focal plane of the condenser the two azimuths (at right angles to each other) of a regularly-arranged object will appear illuminated in the two colours. For example, a textile with a regular warp and weft can be so illuminated that the warp fibres appear coloured red whilst the weft fibres appear as green; similarly, crystal faces arranged at right angles to one another may be displayed in different colours. For certain specialist purposes this technique may possess definite advantages. The introduction of colour photomicrography appears to have given Rheinberg illumination a new lease of life for the production of photomicrographs intended for the illustration of book jackets or record sleeves.

2.3   Phase contrast microscopy

In any type of microscopy the specimen has a profound effect on the light passing through it; for example there may be a change in amplitude, a change in the phase of the light waves or some alteration of their plane of vibration. In conventional direct microscopy the dyes used to colour the specimen cause absorption of some of the light so that there is in this case an amplitude change. This is manifested as a change in intensity (intensity is proportional to the square of the amplitude). In the examination of anisotropic materials with the polarizing microscope (section 3.2) the specimen affects the vibration plane of the light with consequent effects on the image obtained. Some objects, such as transparent living cells, do not affect either the amplitude or the vibration direction of the light passing through them. They do, however, affect the phase relationships of the light waves to an extent dependent upon the difference between the refractive index of the specimen and the mounting medium and upon the thickness of the object itself. This change in phase (φ) is a retardation if the object has a higher refractive index than the mountant and is expressed by the equation

$$\varphi = (n_o - n_m) t$$

where n_o = the refractive index of the object, n_m = the refractive index of the mounting medium and t is the thickness of the object.

The human eye is not sensitive to differences in the phase of light waves, so that objects which exhibit such a phase change in the microscope will not show any contrast unless the phase change can be converted into an amplitude change by optical means. This is accomplished by the phase contrast microscope (invented by F. Zernike, for which he eventually received the Nobel prize in 1953). The principle of the phase contrast microscope is relatively simple and may be explained in non-mathematical terms.

We have seen in the first chapter that the microscope image is formed by the interference and interaction of the direct light with that diffracted by the object itself, i.e. light which may be considered to originate at the plane of the specimen. In a stained specimen the phase difference between the direct beam and the diffracted light is 180° so that they will interfere destructively. If the direct beam is represented by the curve **DL** in Fig. 2–4a and the diffracted light by the curve **DF**, then the resultant will be represented by the bold line **R**. It can be seen that this differs from the original direct light in that it is of reduced amplitude and this gives the contrast necessary for visualization of the object. This situation may also be expressed in the form of a vector diagram (Fig. 2–4b) where the direction of the line represents the phase of the light and the length of the line its amplitude. Again, with a pure amplitude object the resultant **R** is seen to be unchanged in phase but of reduced amplitude.

If we now consider a transparent object there is of course no amplitude change but there is a phase change (φ) introduced by the object. On a vector diagram, therefore, the lines representing the direct beam and the resultant would be of equal length but displaced by an angle equal to that

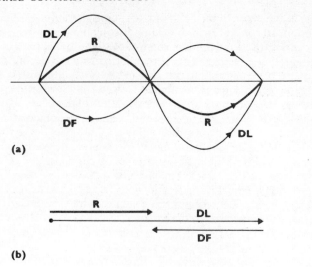

(a)

(b)

Fig. 2–4 (a) Diagram of the direct, diffracted and resultant waves in direct microscopy: (b) Vector diagram of image formation in direct microscopy. **DL** = direct wave. **R** = resultant. **DF** = diffracted wave.

of the phase change φ. This is shown in Fig. 2–5 where the line **OA** represents the direct light and **OB** is the resultant. From the diagram it is apparent that the line **AB** represents the diffracted light which is out of phase with the direct light by the angle OAB; this angle is nearly 90° ($= 1/4\lambda$). In order to achieve amplitude contrast in this situation the vector **OB** must be made smaller than **OA**. This is possible if a *further* phase change of 90° is introduced for the diffracted wave relative to that of the direct light. In the diagram this may be represented by advancing the phase of the direct light, i.e. by rotating the vector **OA** counterclockwise to a new position **OA'**. The diffracted wave remains unchanged so that it is still drawn parallel to **AB** but its origin is now A' not A. Interference between the new direct wave **OA'** and the diffracted wave **A'B'** provides the resultant **OB'** which has a much reduced amplitude; this gives us the necessary contrast and the object, although it is, of course, transparent, *appears* much darker than the background. Had we retarded the direct light with respect to the diffracted beam then the contrast of the object would have been reversed, i.e. it would have appeared bright on a dark background. Both of these situations are used in practice, although the former (positive phase contrast) is favoured.

These optical manipulations are carried out in the actual phase-contrast microscope by means of the 'phase plate' which is built into the back focal plane of the objective. The phase plate is a disc of glass with an annular groove (Fig. 2–6) cut into it. The direct light is obtained from a substage condenser equipped with an annular diaphragm placed in its front focal plane so that the diaphragm is located in a plane conjugate with that of the phase plate. This means that the annulus in the diaphragm can be imaged sharply upon the groove in the phase plate (Fig. 2–7). When the annulus is carefully centred so that its image is exactly coincident with the groove in the phase plate, all the direct light passes through this region of the phase plate. The depth of the groove is so calculated to impart the necessary advance of 90° to the direct light with respect to the

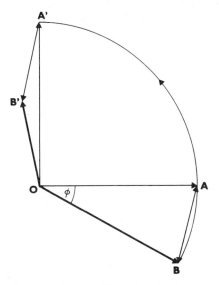

Fig. 2–5   Vector diagram of image formation in phase contrast microscopy. φ = phase change introduced by the object. **OA** = vector representing direct light. **OB** = vector representing resultant beam. **AB** = vector representing diffracted light. **OA'** = vector representing direct light with phase altered. **OB'** = vector representing new resultant beam. **A'B'** = vector representing new diffracted beam.

diffracted light. As this latter arises from the specimen which does not lie in a focal plane conjugate with that of the phase plate, the diffracted waves pass through the whole area of the phase plate, the greater part of which is much thicker than the groove through which the direct light is passing. There is already $1/4\lambda$ phase difference between the direct and diffracted light (introduced by the action of the specimen itself), so that passage of the diffracted light through the thicker area of the phase plate will increase this disparity to approximately $1/2\lambda$, in consequence of which destructive interference may now take place in the primary image plane to give the desired amplitude contrast in the image.

It will be appreciated that each objective requires its own phase plate

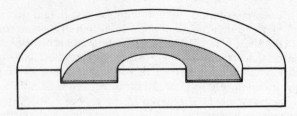

Fig. 2–6   A cut-away diagram of a phase plate. Notice the annular groove with a layer of vacuum-deposited metal on its floor to reduce the intensity of the direct light.

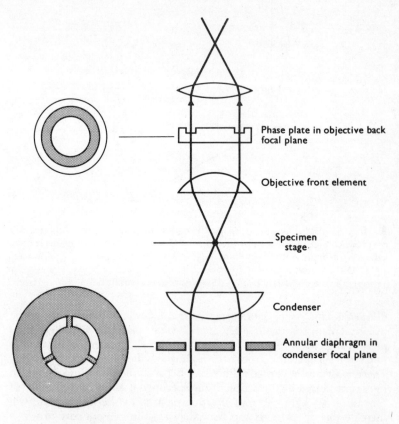

Phase plate in objective back focal plane

Objective front element

Specimen stage·

Condenser

Annular diaphragm in condenser focal plane

Fig. 2–7   The optical system of a phase contrast microscope. The annular diaphragm in the condenser focal plane appears sharply focused on the annular groove in the phase plate, because they are in conjugate focal planes.

and that each of these has a groove of differing size from that in the other lenses. This means that a series of illuminating annuli of different sizes must be provided in the substage condenser. These annuli are often mounted in a rotating wheel or turret which allows easy selection and alignment of the relevant diaphragm. In older phase-contrast microscopes it was necessary to remove the eyepiece in order to see the image of the annulus and the groove in the phase plate in order to align the two. Many modern instruments are now fitted with an accessory lens in the body of the microscope which when inserted into the optical path converts the eyepiece into a viewing telescope for the examination of the back focal plane of the objective; the extra magnification introduced by this system allows very accurate alignment of the image of the annulus with the phase plate.

The contrast of the phase image is usually high. It may, however, be controlled to some extent by using objectives with phase plates of differing characteristics. For example, the degree by which the direct light is advanced may be varied; again, the direct light may be attenuated by an absorbent coating of metal deposited on the floor of the groove in the phase plate. The phase-contrast microscope is relatively cheap and in practice it is easy to use, but the phase image does suffer from optical imperfections, the most noticeable of which is the halo. As the direct and diffracted light are never completely separated in the instrument it will be apparent that some of the diffracted light will pass through the groove in the phase plate along with the direct light; this results in the edges of objects appearing to be surrounded with a bright halo (Fig. 2–8).

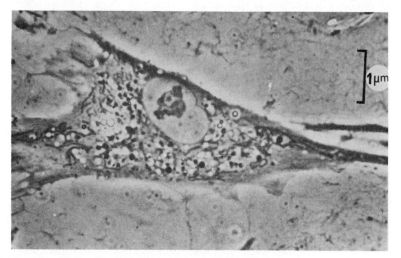

Fig. 2–8   A living fibroblast, in culture, shown by the phase-contrast microscope. Note the marked 'halo' round intracellular droplets.

Although this halo may be of some value in drawing attention to the presence of small objects, e.g. bacteria, it can be a drawback when for example the diameter of a structure is to be measured accurately. One further consequence of the incomplete separation of the direct and diffracted light is that the phase-contrast microscope is relatively insensitive to slow changes in phase. This results in the phase contrast effect being accentuated at discontinuities where there is a marked change in refractive index.

Measurement of the phase change is not easy with the phase-contrast microscope; in addition the inability to vary the degree and type of contrast obtained provide a further restriction upon the use of this instrument other than as a means of increasing the contrast. For quantitative measurements the related interference microscope (section 3.3) is preferable. For many studies on cellular morphology and on those cellular activities which do not demand the highest possible resolution, the phase-contrast microscope can be invaluable. Since 1950 it has been regarded as a routine method which, however, seldom forms the sole, or indeed the principal, tool used in a biological investigation. Many papers have been published on cell division based on information obtained by means of the phase-contrast microscope often combined with the use of time-lapse ciné photomicrography to record the results and to increase the apparent speed of the process. Other phenomena studied with this technique have been phagocytosis and pinocytosis, together with the growth and regeneration of nerve fibres in tissue culture, It is when such dynamic events are being studied that the value of phase-contrast microscopy becomes truly apparent; the growing cells may be kept under ideal conditions of culture and observed whenever necessary without undue disturbance. Excellent accounts of the type of work possible with phase contrast and some results obtained are given in *Cinemicrography in Cell Biology* edited by G. G. Rose and in the book on blood cell cytology by Bessis, both of which are listed in the bibliography.

It will be remembered that the development of a phase change in the light passing through an object depends not only upon the thickness of the object but also upon the difference in refractive index between the object itself and the surrounding mounting medium. If this difference is reduced to zero, i.e. the object is mounted in a medium of the same refractive index as itself, the contrast obtainable is also reduced to zero and the object becomes invisible. Should the refractive index of the medium be made higher than that of the object then the object will again become visible but with a reversed or 'bright' contrast. This principle has been used in the technique called 'immersion refractometry'. With this technique it is possible to determine the mean refractive index (and hence the solid concentration, see section 3.2) of a population of cells. This is done by immersing them in a series of media of differing refractive indices and finding the refractive index of that medium in which there are equal numbers of cells appearing bright and dark. Immersion refractometry has not been very extensively used in biology, possibly because the need to make up numbers of media of different refractive indices is laborious and because the sensitivity of the method is limited. Interference microscopy is without question the method of choice for quantitative measurements on transparent preparations such as living cells.

In the last few months Hoffman and Gross have published descriptions of a new microscope system which they term 'modulation contrast'. This reveals phase gradients in a specimen by means of a special filter or 'modulator' placed in the back focal plane of the objective where it is conjugate with a slit aperture in the front focal plane of the condenser. The modulator has three strips of differing optical transmission arranged so that there is one dark region, one grey region and a light area. When the image of the slit is registered on the grey region, light passing through regions of the specimen where there are no gradients must pass through the grey area of the modulator (where its intensity is reduced to a fraction of its former value) before reaching the image plane where it forms the overall grey background. Light passing through a positive gradient in the specimen is refracted mostly into the light area of the modulator so giving bright features in the image and, conversely, negative gradients in the specimen direct rays through the darkest area of the modulator which attenuates them to form the dark features in the image. This process thus gives an 'optical shadowing' or an illusion of three dimensions resembling that obtained with Nomarski-type interference contrast. The modulation contrast technique has the advantage of great simplicity and may easily be added to any microscope. Further details may be found in the articles by Hoffman and Gross quoted in the bibliography.

2.4   Fluorescence microscopy

It has long been known that certain compounds possess the property of absorbing short wavelength radiation (either in the blue, violet or ultra-violet regions of the spectrum) and re-emitting the energy as light of a longer wavelength. If the emission of these longer wavelengths only continues throughout the period of excitation, then the phenomenon is called 'fluorescence'; if the light emission persists for an appreciable time after stopping the excitation, then we have 'phosphorescence'. The colour of the fluorescence is independent of the wavelength of the exciting radiation although it is well known that the efficiency of various wavelengths in exciting the fluorescence of a given compound varies considerably. Fluorescence is a labile phenomenon. Often it is found that the intensity of the emitted radiation falls off very rapidly due to the exciting radiation causing actual changes in the fluorescent compound itself; again, traces of contaminants (especially those of heavy metals such as iron or mercury) or changes in the pH of the mounting medium may markedly affect the intensity of the fluorescence by causing what is known as 'quenching' of the fluorescence.

The fluorescence microscope is essentially a conventional optical microscope stand, operating either in transmitted or, very often nowadays, in the incident light mode. With the transmitted light version the dark ground type of illumination is usually employed, as this method concentrates the short wavelength radiation on the specimen and allows one to obtain a much darker background for the fluorescent image and so a much brighter fluorescent image than would be the case if a full cone of illumination were used. The optical arrangement of a typical transmitted light fluorescence microscope is shown in diagrammatic form in Fig. 2-9.

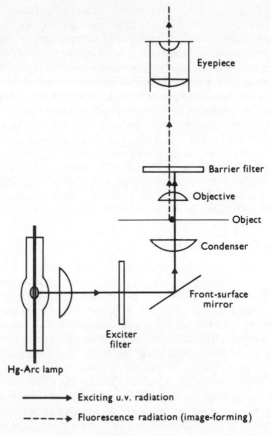

Fig. 2-9 The optical arrangement of a transmitted light fluorescence microscope. The heavy line represents the optical path of the exciting radiation, the dotted line represents the path of the emitted fluorescence radiation.

The exciting light is provided by a high intensity lamp which emits radiation in the required regions of the spectrum. Often the lamp of choice is a high-intensity mercury arc but occasionally low-voltage tungsten lamps will suffice for certain applications. The radiation of the correct wavelength is isolated by passing the beam through what is termed the 'exciter' filter and passed via an aluminized front-surface mirror into the condenser. After inducing fluorescence in the specimen, the exciting radiation has served its purpose and is no longer needed. The optical system, therefore, contains a second filter (between the objective and the eyepiece) which acts as a barrier to the passage of the short wave exciting radiation but allows the longer wavelength fluorescence to pass and form the image of the object. In this type of microscopy the image of the object is formed entirely by light rays which actually emanate in the object itself and so any fluorescent specimen appears as if it were self-luminous, standing out very brightly upon a dark background. It is obvious that in order to obtain satisfactory images of fluorescent specimens as much of the exciting radiation as possible must be concentrated on the object and for this reason high aperture dark ground condensers are usually fitted for transmission fluorescence microscopy. Similarly, it follows that the correct wavelength of exciting radiation must be employed; if the fluorescent substance under examination has its emission maximum (the wavelength at which the intensity of the fluorescence is greatest) widely separated from the wavelength at which maximal excitation occurs then it is relatively simple to choose correct combinations of exciter and barrier filters to allow maximal absorption of exciting energy and minimal absorption of the longer wavelength fluorescent emission. In this case it is usual to use standard wide-band transmission filters for both purposes. With ultra-violet excitation the exciting filter is almost opaque to all visible radiation (for example a Schott UG1 filter) whilst the barrier filter is a very pale yellow. Only if the wavelength of maximal excitation is very close to the wavelength of maximal emission of fluorescence is it necessary to use special narrow band interference filters, often in conjunction with a second set of standard glass filters. This will allow excitation with a very narrow and clearly defined band of wavelengths and at the same time the narrow transmission of the barrier filter set will allow observation of the fluorescence image without disturbance from the exciting radiation. With such narrow band widths for excitation, much less energy falls on the specimen and hence there is often a considerable falling off in the intensity of the final image. It is also possible for some purposes to use exciting radiation in the blue region of the spectrum (the so-called 'blue light' fluorescence); in this case the barrier filter is a deep orange in colour and the fluorescence image appears with a distorted colour rendering.

Recently there has been a trend towards the use of incident light fluorescence techniques, originally developed by J. S. Ploem. These differ from the transmission methods in that the exciting radiation is concentrated on the object from above, the objective serving as its own condenser (Fig. 2–10). Only that area of the object under examination is irradiated at any one time; furthermore, as the exciting radiation impinges on the surface of the specimen there are no losses of fluorescence by absorption within the thickness of the specimen, the

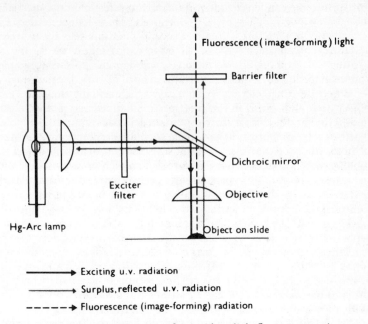

Fluorescence (image-forming) light

Barrier filter

Dichroic mirror

Exciter filter

Objective

Hg-Arc lamp

Object on slide

⟶ Exciting u.v. radiation

⟶ Surplus, reflected u.v. radiation

---⟶ Fluorescence (image-forming) radiation

Fig. 2–10   The optical arrangement of an incident-light fluorescence microscope using a vertical illuminator with dichroic mirror.

emitted radiation arising from the most superficial parts of the specimen. This means that the image in incident light fluorescence is usually brighter than if the transmission mode were used. Such vertical fluorescence illuminators are now available from several different makers but all are constructed upon the same general principle. The exciting radiation, either blue light or ultra-violet radiation, is passed through the exciter filter and is reflected downwards into the optical axis of the microscope and into the back of the objective by means of a dichroic mirror mounted in a turret. Often three or four different dichroic mirrors and barrier filters are provided in a rotating turret so that the correct filter combinations for any type of fluorescence may be selected very easily and quickly. The dichroic mirror reflects the short wavelength exciting radiation into the objective which acts as its own condenser and concentrates the illumination on the surface of the specimen. The longer wavelength emitted radiation, however, emanating from the specimen, passes into the objective and up the optical axis of the instrument, passing straight through the dichroic mirror which is transparent to these longer wavelengths. Following the dichroic mirror is the correct barrier filter which prevents any of the exciting radiation interfering with the fluorescent image. The incident light fluorescence attachment has an added advantage in that other methods of illumination may be applied to the same specimen at the same time. For example, it is possible to use incident light fluorescence to detect the presence of, say, 5-hydroxytryptamine whilst at the same time observing the same specimen with transmitted light phase-contrast illumination in order to ascertain the location of the fluorescent material. Transmitted light excitation with ultra-violet light may be used and at the same time combined with incident light excitation with blue light, in order to observe the different fluorescence colours produced by differing types of substance under these conditions whilst other possible combinations exist for special applications.

Fluorescence exhibited by microscopical objects may be classified into two main categories—primary or 'autofluorescence' and secondary. The latter may be further subdivided into 'induced' fluorescence, when the compound is converted into a fluorescent substance (or 'fluorophore') by a specific chemical reaction performed on the tissue, and into that fluorescence produced by the action of 'fluorochroming' the material in the section by the action of a fluorescent dye-stuff. Finally, and perhaps to the biologist the most important, we have those reactions which are classified as 'fluorescent antibody reactions' in which the site of an antigen-antibody reaction is made visible by labelling one of the participants (either antigen or antibody) with a fluorescent dye.

Autofluorescence is the natural fluorescence of the substances present naturally in the tissues; it is present to some small degree in almost all tissue components. In animal tissues, for example, collagen, elastin and some pigments (the lipofuscins) show an intense autofluorescence in common with proteins rich in the amino acids tryptophane, tyrosine and phenyl alanine. In some cases the autofluorescent colours may be of use in locating particular compounds. For example, although the general colour of autofluorescence is a pale blue or blue-green, porphyrins in animal tissues and chlorophyll in plants both show a very strong red fluorescence when irradiated by ultra-violet light. Substances which may be directly identified and located by the fluorescence microscope are so few, however, that this application of the instrument is only of limited value; the real use of the fluorescence microscope is in the fields of induced fluorescence.

Induced fluorescence is the situation which is found when a compound which by itself does not fluoresce is converted by some specific chemical

treatment to another which does. At present the most important reaction
in this category is the induction of fluorescence by condensing various
amines with formaldehyde. The formaldehyde-induced fluorescence is a
very valuable technique for locating substances such as Dopa, dopamine,
catecholamine, adrenalin and 5-hydroxytryptamine. All of these
substances are of great pharmacological interest; in this field
formaldehyde-induced fluorescence is much used in the location of
adrenalin and noradrenalin in the nerve terminations of the autonomic
nervous system. Figure 2–11 shows the fluorescence of the nerve terminals
in the vasomotor innervation of the iris diaphragm of the eye of a rat.

Fig. 2–11   A fluorescence micrograph of the nerve terminations in the iris
diaphragm of a rat eye. The strong contrast is due to formaldehyde-induced
fluorescence of the noradrenaline in the nerve terminals.

Other techniques of induced fluorescence with known chemical
specificities have recently been developed by Stoward and his co-workers.
By using his techniques, many mucosubstances may be positively
identified and located in the tissues. Such methods have an advantage
over the conventional histochemical techniques in that the fluorescent
image appears brightly coloured on a dark background, and hence the
image contrast is high. At the same time the sensitivity of many
fluorescence methods is higher than that of the corresponding
histochemical staining reaction so that much smaller amounts of the
compound may be located.

It is possible to use simple fluorescent dyes in the same manner as an ordinary biological stain; these compounds are then termed 'fluorochromes'. Many fluorochromes are coloured and so the tissues stained by them may also be examined conventionally in transmitted light. It is generally possible to reveal the presence of very small amounts of fluorochrome and so these compounds are used in very low concentrations (solutions of 1 part in 10 000 or even less are not uncommon) and therefore fluorochromes may often be used on living cells without any toxic effects becoming apparent. Many dyes are now in use as fluorochromes but special mention may be made of the application of the dye Acridine Orange in studies of tumour cells. In such cells the concentration of cytoplasmic ribonucleic acid is often very high; as this substance shows a vivid orange-red fluorescence with Acridine Orange whilst the nuclear deoxyribonucleic acid shows a greenish yellow colour, the distinction between these two types of nucleic acid is made very easy. At the same time a rough guess may be made of their relative concentrations. Acridine Orange is often used in the field of exfoliative cytology where the abnormal cells in the smear preparation stand out clearly from the surrounding normal cells which do not show any significant cytoplasmic RNA concentration and hence do not have the red cytoplasmic fluorescence.

One recent interesting development of fluorochroming is in the study of human metaphase chromosomes in order to analyse the karyotype and identify individual chromosomes. Caspersson and his colleagues have developed a method based on the binding of a fluorescent compound such as quinacrine or quinacrine mustard to the base part of the DNA molecules found in the chromosomes. Differences in the local amounts of DNA along the chromosome and differences in the extent to which the DNA is accessible to the quinacrine mustard result in the formation of a typical detailed binding pattern peculiar to each individual chromosome. So characteristic is the staining pattern that even specific regions of an individual chromosome may be located with certainty. A method is thus available at last which allows the cytogeneticist to do with human chromosomes what has hitherto only been possible with the large polytene chromosomes of the Diptera, i.e. recognize specific chromosomal regions by a staining technique. By the use of fluorescence staining, chromosome abnormalities may now be studied in great detail. For example, three well-known trisomy conditions exist in man in which the chromosome duplication occurs either in the D or in the G group of chromosomes. Fluorescence analysis has enabled geneticists to identify the duplicate chromosome and say in each case whether it is number 13, 18 or 21. Structural aberrations may also be shown up with this new technique. Patients suffering from chronic myeloid leukemia, for example, show a peculiar extra chromosome—the Philadelphia chromosome—in their karyotypes. For many years this extra chromosome has been a mystery but the banding pattern revealed by the fluorescence microscope proves conclusively that the Philadelphia chromosome is the result of a deletion in chromosome 22. Similarly, translocations have now been located in the karyotype of healthy subjects where perhaps the long arm of one chromosome is broken off at the centromere and attached to a neighbouring chromosome. Translocation between homologous chromosomes must introduce a large risk that any offspring of that individual might suffer from an unbalanced chromosomal complement with a consequent congenital defect. Knowledge of this type may well in future become of great importance with the spread of genetic counselling.

It has been reported that quinacrine mustard induces a bright fluorescence in the long arm of the Y chromosome found in males. This enhanced fluorescence appears as a bright dot in preparations of the interphase nucleus. Y-bearing spermatozoa also show this extra fluorescence, so that fluorescence microscopy has now been added as a valuable aid in the analysis of the Y sex chromatin in just the same way that studies of the Barr body with conventional staining techniques allows an investigation of the nuclear X chromatin content. A reference to this new method of chromosomal analysis is given in the bibliography (see Caspersson *et al.*, 1972).

Fluorescent antibody methods, forming the techniques of 'immuno-fluorescence', have been extensively developed since the early work of Coons and his associates in the 1940s. The principle of the method is as follows. When a foreign protein (an antigen) is introduced into the body there is a defensive response on the part of the body by the secretion of a neutralizing protein (the antibody) from the cells of the lymphoid system. The antibody combines with the antigen forming a harmless antigen-antibody complex. If now a label, such as a dye, can be attached to an antibody without impairing its efficiency for agglutinating the antigen then we could by simple observation under the microscope learn where the antigen was located in the tissue. In fact, although ordinary dyes have been tried, Coons showed that fluorescent compounds used as markers had several advantages; for example they showed the characteristic fluorescence colour in very low concentrations so that only minute quantities of label were needed. If a fluorescent-labelled antibody to any given protein is added to a tissue section it will combine with any undenatured target protein present in that section. If the surplus labelled-antibody is now washed away and the preparation examined under the fluorescence microscope the sites of antigen-antibody reaction will appear as the only sites showing the characteristic fluorescence colour of the label. This method has the great advantage that, providing a suitable antibody can be prepared, there is a very specific labelling and so a very precise localization may be achieved. This method is the so-called 'direct method' and is illustrated in diagrammatic form in Fig. 2–12.

More refined methods have since been developed, including an

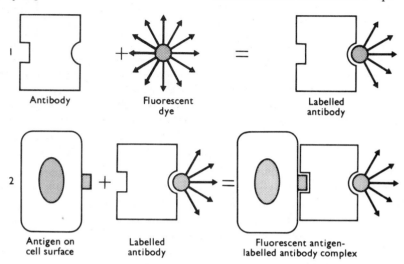

Fig. 2–12   A diagram to illustrate the sequence of events in the 'direct' method of fluorescent antibody labelling.

indirect technique which has an extra stage. In this method the antigen in the cell is complexed as before with the antibody. As this is itself a protein (a γ globulin) it can in turn be used as an antigen and can be further complexed with a second 'anti-γ globulin'. The original antibody is then lying between the two layers of the original antigen and the anti-γ globulin like the meat in a sandwich (Fig. 2–13a). If we now couple a fluorescent dye to the anti-γ globulin we are able to localize the antibody and in turn the original antigen. The great advantage of this procedure with respect to the direct method is that the intensity of the fluorescence may be much increased. This is because several molecules of labelled anti-γ globulin may be attached to the antibody (Fig. 2–13b) and so the intensity of the final fluorescence will be increased by comparison with the direct method in which often only one fluorescent label attaches to an antigen-antibody reaction site.

Many applications of the fluorescent antibody method could be cited but as an example the use of the technique to localize native antigens will be used. It was well known that the cells of the anterior lobe of the pituitary (the adenohypophysis) were responsible for the secretion into the bloodstream of several different hormones, among them being the follicle stimulating and luteinizing hormones, thyrotrophic hormones and adrenocorticotrophic hormone or ACTH. Classical methods of cytology revealed that there were several differing cell types in the adenohypophysis and the problem was to equate these with the hormones which they secreted. It is possible to prepare an antibody to, say, ACTH and to couple this anti-ACTH with fluoroscein isothiocyanate. When this is done the labelled antibody may be applied to sections of the adenohypophysis, the surplus washed away and the preparation examined with ultra-violet light to determine the location of the fluoroscein compound. As the labelled antigen is only bound to sites where ACTH is found in the cells it is thus possible to locate this compound with certainty and to determine which of the cell types is responsible for its production.

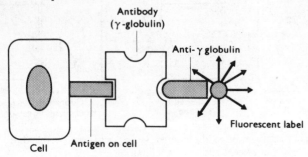

(a) Indirect or sandwich labelling

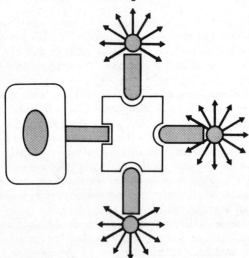

(b) Multiple attachment of anti-γ globulin to antibody

Fig. 2–13 (a) A diagram to illustrate the sequence of events in 'indirect' or 'sandwich' labelling; only one labelled molecule of anti-γ globulin is attached to the antibody. (b) The intensity of the fluorescence may be enhanced by multiple coupling of labelled anti-γ globulin to the antibody.

3 The Microscope as an Analytical Tool

3.1 Introduction

We have seen in the previous chapter how the low contrast images typical of biological material may be enhanced for microscopical examination. Such images, with high resolution of detail, may then be used purely for the examination of the shape of the object and for determining the inter-relationships of its various parts. For nearly three hundred years, biological microscopy regarded this as the limit of its usefulness.

A little thought will show that the image produced by the microscope contains far more information than the simple morphological relationships. Measurements of length, area and number are of great value; such numerical values can now provide the basis for exact statistical comparisons between specimens. For example, instead of saying that the nuclei in a sample of tissue from a tumour appear larger than those in the corresponding normal tissue, we can now answer the question 'How much larger are the abnormal nuclei than the normal?' and determine the statistical significance of the difference between the normal and the abnormal.

Numerical values for projected areas, surface area/volume ratios, optical densities and refractive indices can now all be determined and permit the evaluation of a biological system much more precisely than formerly, when only simple qualitative statements were available. It is now also possible to use the microscope to investigate structures actually below the limits of resolution. An example of this is provided by the effect which any submicroscopic orientation of micelles has on the plane of polarized light passing through the tissue. This can be detected by the use of the polarizing microscope. Similarly, variations in the refractive index cells or their components may be detected and measured with the interference microscope and the data thus obtained used to determine the dry mass of the cell and its changes during biological activity.

In the past, great limitations have been placed on the use of the microscope as a quantitative tool by the inadequacy of the human eye and brain as devices for handling numerical data. Developments of space-age technology, in the form of solid state electronics and miniature integrated circuits, have changed the whole field of quantitative microscopy. Automated methods are now becoming pre-eminent in this field and this development may well ensure that quantitation of the microscope image becomes one of the growing points in microscopy during the next decade.

3.2   The polarizing microscope

Light is normally regarded as a propagated wave motion in which the vibration planes of the waves may assume any angle to the direction of propagation. If the vibration planes are all constrained so that they lie with their displacements parallel and perpendicular to the direction of propagation of the light then plane polarized light results. With the development of polarizing filters, such as 'Polaroid', it is now easy to obtain plane polarized light. Any microscope may thus be converted into a polarizing microscope by placing a 'Polaroid' sheet in any convenient position beneath the substage condenser, so that the object is illuminated with plane polarized light. A second sheet of 'Polaroid' arranged with its vibration direction at right angles to the first sheet acts as an analyser; this may be placed at any convenient position above the objective. In practice the analyser is usually at or just above the back focal plane of the objective or just above the Ramsden circle of the eyepiece.

Such a simple modification will enable many observations to be made in polarized light, although microscopes especially designed for this work have extra refinements such as the provision of a rotating stage graduated in degrees, the provision of slots in the microscope body (above the objective and below the analyser) for the insertion of compensating plates and a cross-wire graticule in the eyepiece. Often an accessory lens (known as a Bertrand lens) is provided, together with some mechanism to introduce it at will into the image train. The Bertrand lens and the eyepiece act together as a short-focus telescope to provide an enlarged image of the back focal plane of the objective. This is desirable in order to examine the interference figures produced in this plane when using a special form of illumination known as 'conoscopic'; this type of illumination, however, is principally used by crystallographers and will not be considered further here.

When unpolarized light, with its wave trains vibrating in all planes, enters anisotropic or birefringent objects it becomes converted into two beams with their planes of vibration orientated at right angles to one another (Fig. 3–1a). One of these beams satisfies Snell's law of refraction and hence is termed the 'ordinary' ray; for this ray the refractive index of the medium (n_o) is the same at any direction of incidence. The second or 'extraordinary' ray has its plane of vibration at right angles to that of the ordinary ray and for this ray the refractive index of the material (n_E) is a function of the direction of the ray in the material. In one particular direction the refractive index for the extraordinary ray is equal to that of the ordinary ray, and along this direction (the optical axis) the two beams are not physically separated (Fig. 3–1b). The maximum difference in

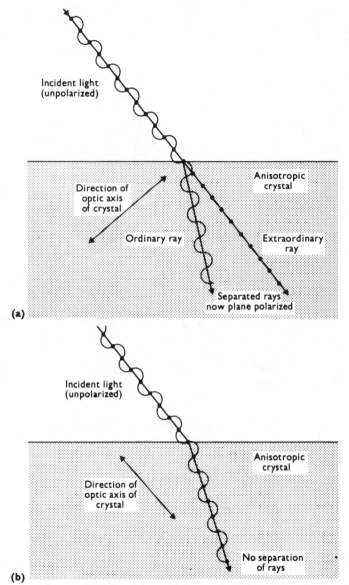

Fig. 3–1 (a) The behaviour of a beam of unpolarized light entering an anisotropic object at right angles to the optical axis. Separation into two beams, each plane polarized, results. (b) No separation into ordinary and extraordinary rays occurs when the beam of light enters an anisotropic object *along* the optical axis.

refractive index of the material for the two rays is when the light is incident at right angles to the optical axis. In this position the difference in the refractive indices for the ordinary and extraordinary ray is termed the 'birefringence' of the material and it is positive if $n_E > n_o$, and negative if the converse applies.

Many materials, of course, do not affect light waves in this manner; these are termed 'isotropic' materials. If an isotropic object is viewed with a polarizing microscope, arranged with the vibration directions of polarizer and analyser at right angles to each other, the field of view will appear dark. All the polarized light is prevented from passing by the analyser. When a birefringent or anisotropic object is substituted, however, with its two axes of preferred vibration direction orientated at 45° to the crossed polarizer and analyser, then components of both ordinary and extraordinary rays are produced which vibrate in such a direction that they pass the analyser. The object then appears bright, on a dark field. If the object is rotated its brightness will appear to vary, according to the angle which it makes with the polarizer, passing through four positions of maximal brightness and four positions of darkness for 360° of rotation.

As the speed of light in a body is inversely proportional to the refractive index of that body, it follows that the ordinary and extraordinary rays will travel at different speeds in an anisotropic object; they will thus be out of phase on emerging by a small amount which depends on the thickness of the object and upon the degree of birefringence of the object. When the ordinary and extraordinary rays are brought into the same plane of vibration by the analyser they may thus interfere, and if white light is used to illuminate the object, a small band of wavelengths may be eliminated. This results in the object showing one of the interference colours of what is known as 'Newton's Scale'.

If the thickness of the object is known it is possible, by introducing 'compensators' (birefringent plates of known thickness and retardation) above the object, to determine accurately both the sign and the amount of the birefringence. For details of the use of compensators in polarized light microscopy the text listed in the bibliography may be consulted.

The birefringence of biological materials can be measured whilst the organism is alive and determinations with the polarizing microscope thus often avoid the criticism that the phenomenon under study was introduced or modified by the preparative procedures used. In general birefringence may be due to either:

  (i) the presence of a regular, crystalline structure

 or (ii) to a regular arrangement of submicroscopic rods or micelles embedded in a matrix of different refractive index

or (iii) to the temporary alignment of micelles which occurs during the stressing of a structure or during flowing or streaming of protoplasm.

Crystalline birefringence is usually quite strong; a good example is shown by the birefringence of the calcareous skeletons of Foraminifera or calcareous sponge spicules. Examination with the polarizing microscope with crossed polars thus provides a simple non-destructive method of differentiating calcareous from siliceous skeletons, e.g. Globigerina ooze from Radiolarian ooze or calcareous sponge spicules from the siliceous spicules of the Hexactinellid sponges.

Stress or flow birefringence is usually weak; it may be demonstrated easily in the long siliceous rooting spicules of the sponge *Hyalonema*. If one of these is bent whilst under observation with the polarizing microscope it can be seen to change from the isotropic condition to show anisotropy on its inner and outer axes of curvature.

Birefringence due to the presence of a regular array of submicroscopic rodlets or platelets (Fig. 3.2) is often known as 'form birefringence' and is

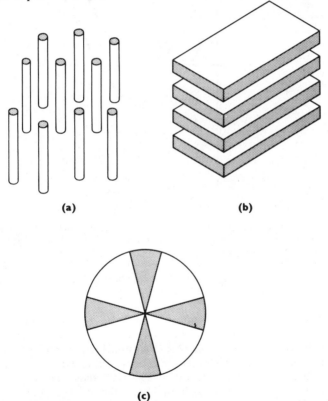

(a)   (b)

(c)

Fig. 3–2   (a) Form birefringence will occur if orientated rodlets are present in a matrix or (b) if parallel platelets occur. (c) This represents the appearance of the Maltese cross of polarization in a droplet containing radial or tangential orientations of micelles.

the most common type of birefringence shown by biological material. If a structure which exhibits form birefringence is immersed successively in media of different refractive indices it will be found that the degree of birefringence varies and will vanish at the point where the refractive index of the mountant is equal to that of the orientated micelles. Plotting the values of birefringence against the refractive index of the medium gives a characteristic U-shaped curve (i in Fig. 3–3).

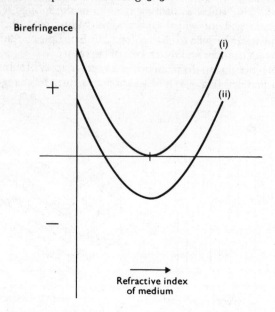

Fig. 3–3   A diagrammatic plot to show the relationship between birefringence and refractive index of the medium for a specimen showing form birefringence. In case (i) the form birefringence disappears when the R.I. of the medium is equal to that of the micelles. In case (ii) there is crystalline birefringence of opposite sign to that of the form birefringence which ensures that there are two points where the total birefringence is zero.

Occasionally form birefringence may be present together with crystalline birefringence. In this case if the refractive index of the mountant is changed only that part of the total birefringence which is due to the orientated submicroscopic micelles will alter whilst the crystalline birefringence will remain unaffected. This latter may even be of opposite sign to the form birefringence, in which case the curve obtained will show two changes in the sign of the total birefringence (ii in Fig. 3–3).

Many studies of form birefringence have been carried out on biological material: two workers deeply involved in this study were Frey-Wyssling (using plant cells) and Inoué, who worked with dividing animal cells. Frey-

Wyssling used the strong birefringence of the cellulose fibrils in the plant cell wall to study their orientation. In some of the technologically important bast fibres he found the fibril direction was parallel to the axis of the elongated cells. Fibres of ramie, which are pure cellulose, show this effect and from a study of this plant the optical constants of the cellulose fibre were accurately determined. Flax and hemp have a similar fibril pattern. Much more common, however, was the helical arrangement of fibres found in the cell walls of cotton and of Gymnosperm tracheids. In this last example the bordered pits show a special type of birefringence characteristic of the radial or tangential orientations found in spherites. This phenomenon appears as a dark cross (the cross of polarization) (Fig. 3–2c) which is independent of the orientation of the spherite under the microscope. Other examples of objects possessing the spherite type of organization are starch grains and some phospholipid droplets found in animal cells and these also show the cross of polarization. This has proved of some diagnostic importance in histochemical work.

The majority of animal cells have isotropic cytoplasm, implying no regular arrangement of submicroscopic micelles, although when streaming occurs a type of stress birefringence may appear. This is often only slight and a very sensitive polarizing microscope is required to detect it. Such flow birefringence is postulated to be due to an alignment of the long chain micelles consequent upon the formation of a pseudopodium. Stronger birefringence, however, appears in the astral rays and in the spindle of the mitotic figure. Work by Inoué and others has shown that the birefringence of the spindle is strongest during metaphase, declining markedly during the succeeding anaphase. Polarizing studies on living dividing cells led to the postulate that the spindle was composed of a parallel arrangment of protein fibres radiating from the centrosomes. This has since been amply confirmed with the electron microscopical demonstration of the microtubules which constitute the mitotic spindle.

Valuable help has been obtained from the polarizing microscope in the examination of the strongly birefringent 'A band' region in striated muscle fibres. Long before the parallel array of myosin filaments could be seen with the electron microscope their existence had been deduced from the polarization phenomenon. Similarly, much information has been gathered about the organization of the myelin of nerve sheaths and of collagen fibres in tendon. Although direct visualization of such structures with the electron microscope has now tended to eclipse the value of polarization microscopy, nevertheless the fact that the latter can operate on fresh material still ensures its continued use in biological research.

3.3   The interference microscope

It was pointed out in section 2.3 on phase contrast microscopy that light passing through a transparent object, such as a living cell, is retarded in phase with respect to light from the same source which has passed through the medium around the object. This change of phase (the optical path difference) is used in the phase contrast microscope to provide the image contrast for the visualization of structural details. In the related interference microscope it is possible not only to obtain visual contrast in transparent living material but also to measure easily and directly the optical path difference. From such measurements simple calculations will provide the refractive index and the dry mass of the cell; in consequence the interference microscope has sometimes been called the 'cell biologists' microbalance'.

Some current interference microscopes work on a system developed originally by Jamin and Lebedeff; the light is polarized and split into the main and reference beams by means of a birefringent plate mounted above the condenser. This plate produces two laterally separated beams with their vibration directions perpendicular to each other and at 45° to the plane of vibration of the polarized light which enters the condenser. After passing through the object plane, the two beams are recombined by a second birefringent plate, of equal but opposite sign, mounted on the front of the objective. The optical system is so arranged that one of the beams (the 'object' beam) passes through the object and the other (the 'reference' beam) passes through a clear area of the preparation. Any path difference introduced by the specimen will result in phase change in the object beam and this is expressed as subsequent interference when the beams are recombined. By a suitable arrangement of the optical system it is possible to produce a series of dark fringes crossing the field of view (Fig. 3–4a). The presence of a phase change due to the object then appears as a lateral displacement of the fringes (Fig. 3–4b). Measurement of the amount of fringe displacement can be used to determine the degree of phase-change introduced by the object. Such single-objective interference microscopes in which the reference beam passes to one side of the object (and also the related 'double-focus' type (Fig. 3–5) where the reference beam is brought to a plane of focus above that of the main object beam) suffer from the drawback that the size of object from which accurate measurements can be obtained is very limited. If the object occupies more than a quarter of the field of view it will also, of necessity, be traversed by the reference beam (which should avoid it altogether) and invalid results will be obtained. Other types of interference microscopes are made, one of which, originally due to Nomarski, uses modified Wollaston prisms to divide and recombine the beams; this instrument gives a remarkable pseudo-relief effect to preparations examined with it.

Interference microscopes have several advantages with respect to phase contrast instruments. Firstly their optical systems are so arranged that the direct light which acts as a reference beam is completely separated from the diffracted light which has had its phase changed by the object. This means that the prominent 'halo' artifact and the 'shading' or 'edge'

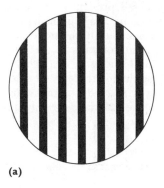

(a)

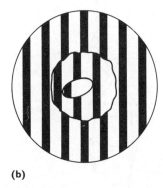

(b)

Fig. 3–4 (a) The appearance of the field of view in an interference microscope. The interference fringes crossing the field of view are all parallel. (b) The same field following the introduction of a transparent object. Note the lateral displacement of the fringes by the cell cytoplasm and nucleus.

artifacts associated with phase contrast are absent. The linearity of conversion of phase changes introduced by the object into intensity differences in the image holds good over a much greater range than for phase contrast instruments so that more accurate renderings of the appearance of living cells are obtained with the interference microscope. The second great advantage of the interference microscope is that accurate quantitative measurements of the phase change can be made with relative ease, whether fringe-field or even-field illumination is used. If white light is used, with an even-field illumination condition then the Newtonian colours in which the object and background appear are extremely valuable. Suppose we are looking for fine structural detail. If this is presented to the eye as a dark grey, seen against a background which is only slightly less dark, then we often have considerable difficulty in appreciating the detail present in the image. Introduce a colour difference, however, and the eye is immediately aware of the difference between, say, a reddish and a bluish hue. It is this sensitivity of the eye which renders the colour contrasts of the interference microscope so useful in microstructural studies. A small change of phase which might not produce a perceptible difference in the image of the phase contrast microscope produces a marked colour change in the image of the interference microscope which can be readily appreciated.

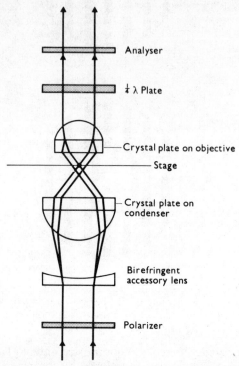

Analyser

$\frac{1}{4}\lambda$ Plate

Crystal plate on objective

Stage

Crystal plate on condenser

Birefringent accessory lens

Polarizer

Fig. 3–5 A diagram of the arrangement of the Jamin-Lebedeff type of interference microscope (Smith/Baker version). The reference beam is brought to a different focal level by means of a birefringent crystal plate mounted on the condenser. The $\frac{1}{4}$ wave plate serves to convert any circularly or elliptically polarized light into plane polarized light. In consequence the resultant beam reaching the compensator is always plane-polarized whether the field is empty or whether one of the beams has been retarded by an object.

The use of the interference microscope in purely qualitative biological research has been slight; the work of G. B. David, using a Jamin-Lebedeff instrument, will serve to illustrate the scope of such studies. He, and his colleagues, have used this type of microscope to identify in living isolated vertebrate nerve cells a cytoplasmic network and cytoplasmic irregular bodies which cannot be seen by any other method of observation. This network has been shown to consist of material with a refractive index of 1.52, corresponding to an average dry mass of 1.03×10^{-12} g μm^{-3}. Such values suggest that the network and associated bodies are made up of arrays of granular and membranous material packed too closely for the individual components to be resolved by optical microscopy. Electron microscopy has confirmed this and the networks and granules seen in the living cell can be equated with the endoplasmic reticulum and the Nissl complex. The interference microscope has thus provided us with very valuable evidence that the structures visualized by the electron micro-scope after the complex techniques of preparation do have a basis in reality in the living cell and are not entirely artifactual, as some experimenters have maintained.

Other workers are introducing the interference microscope into clinical medicine, especially in the field of exfoliative cytology. Here diagnosis of tumour cells or of other cell abnormalities is carried out on specimens of cells obtained from the patients. It is often easier to interpret the images when interference microscopy is used; with phase contrast the halo effect may well obscure just those cytological details which are of great value for diagnosis.

It is in its quantitative application, however, that the interference microscope has been of most use in biology, especially for the determination of the dry mass of cells. The refractive index of a cell is directly related to the concentration of its solids and the phase change produced on passage of a light wave through a cell is related to the product of the refractive index and the thickness of the cell. It follows that if we can measure the refractive index and the thickness we can then calculate the total concentration of the solids present from the expression

$$M = \frac{\varphi . A}{100 . \alpha}$$

where φ is the measured phase change, α is a constant (the 'specific refractive increment', usually taken to have a value of 0.0018), A is the area and M the dry mass of the cell. It should be realized that the value calculated for M/A is that which obtains only at the point in the cytoplasm at which φ, the phase change, was measured. In order to overcome this drawback semiautomatic or automatic integrating instruments have been developed in recent years. These allow the scanning of the whole cell in order to obtain an integrated value of the phase change over the whole cell area (see section 3.5).

Ross used the interference microscope in his studies on the developing spermatids of *Locusta*, particularly on the inclusion body known as the 'Nebenkern'. This is a large body formed by the coalescence of the mitochondria in the spermatocyte. With interference microscopy Ross was able to determine the refractive index of the Nebenkern to be 1.37, from which he calculated its solid content to be between 21 and 26%. Similar studies were carried out on the nucleolus of ascites tumour cells. Here the refractive index was between 1.40 and 1.45, depending on the strain of tumour cell; the corresponding figures for solid concentration were from 39 to 60%.

Such refractive index measurements can sometimes help in the identification of the chemical nature of cell inclusions. For example, if the refractive index of a droplet is very high (e.g. 1.53) then it is extremely likely that the principal component is triglyceride. Some cells, however, contain droplets with a lower refractive index than any pure lipid; the conclusion is that such droplets contain appreciable quantities of hydrophilic lipids (phospholipids) and cholesterol, a conclusion supported by histochemical studies.

As a final example of the type of quantitative data provided by the interference microscope, the studies made by Ross on the nucleoli of developing myoblasts may be quoted. He measured the total mass of nucleolar material per nucleus in uninucleate, bi- and multinucleate myoblasts (Fig. 3–6). It can be seen from this histogram that the nuclei of binucleate cells have less nucleolar material per nucleus than the uninucleate cells and that the multinucleate nuclei have an intermediate position. From these results Ross concluded that during the process of fusion of uninucleate myoblasts to procure the multinucleate 'muscle tube' condition, nucleolar material (possibly ribonucleoprotein) is removed from the nucleoli faster than it can be synthesized, and so some of the nucleoli decrease in dry mass. When cell fusion between myoblasts is completed the synthesis of nucleolar material catches up again and the nucleolar mass therefore increases. As the binucleate cells are the products of the immediate fusion of two uninucleate myoblasts these have low figures whilst the intermediate value reported for multinucleate cells follows from the fact that these are mixtures of recent and less-recent cell fusions.

Similar studies were used to compare the nucleolar masses of uninucleate myoblasts from normal and dystrophic strains of mice. Here marked differences were found, the dystrophic mice having many more nucleoli with a dry mass of less than 0.75 picograms (15–50% of total nucleoli, according to the progression of the condition, as against 4% in a normal mouse). This observation suggests very strongly that in muscular dystrophy the RNA synthetic mechanisms in the nuclei are disturbed; this in its turn would disrupt the normal differentiation of the muscle fibres, a feature which is characteristic of this condition.

These examples show that although at first sight measurement of such quantities as refractive index and dry mass of cellular components does not appear very relevant, nevertheless such data can in many circumstances be of considerable interest in the understanding of

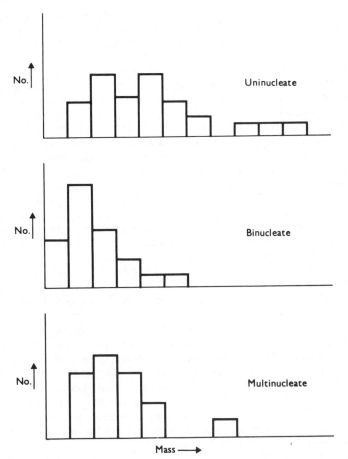

Fig. 3–6 Histograms of the total nucleolar mass in uni-, bi- and multinucleate myoblasts, derived by measurements made with the interference microscope. Data from the work of Ross, 1967.

biological problems which justifies the labour involved in their accurate measurement.

3.4   The microscope as a measuring instrument

Measurement of objects seen under the microscope is very important; a knowledge of the size of an object, e.g. an erythrocyte, may be of great help in establishing the species from which it came or again may provide valuable clues telling us that all is not well. For example, the normal human red blood cell has a diameter of 7.2 μm in the dried film and all the erythrocytes are of similar size within close limits. In pernicious anaemia the presence of erythrocytes of unequal sizes (especially of those large cells called macrocytes) is a very common finding.

Measurements under the microscope may be made on very small samples of tissue and such measurements need not be limited to simple estimates of length or diameter. Methods are available for estimating the number of cells in a given volume of solution, for measuring angles, areas and surface/volume ratios. Length determination may be carried out very simply by projecting the image of the object on to a screen and drawing round its outline. The object is then removed from the microscope and replaced by a stage micrometer (an accurately calibrated scale) which is projected on to the original drawing so that the required length may be read off directly, with ruler or calipers. As an alternative to projection, an 'eyepiece micrometer' is used for routine work. This is a scale of arbitrary divisions engraved on a small glass disc inserted into the focal plane of the eyepiece. As the eye-lens is usually provided with a screw focusing mechanism, the eyepiece can be adjusted so that the lines on the scale appear in focus at the same time as the image of the object. Once the graticule in the eyepiece has been calibrated for any given objective lens it is a simple matter to determine the dimensions of any object by counting the number of graticule divisions which it spans.

A refinement of this system uses what is called a 'filar' eyepiece. This contains a fixed reference hair line together with a moveable hair line driven by a graduated micrometer drum. In use, one end of the object is aligned with the fixed line whilst the moveable marker is moved to span the object. The reading on the micrometer dial then gives a direct measure of the distance moved by the two hair lines, from which the dimensions of the object can be calculated. As with a standard eyepiece micrometer, the filar micrometer eyepiece must be calibrated for the objective in use by matching it against a stage micrometer.

Recently the microscope manufacturers have been attempting to increase the accuracy of length measurements under the microscope. Wild Heerbrugg, for example, have introduced an electronic device (the Tesa attachment) for increasing the precision of length measurements. The measuring probe is built into a filar eyepiece so arranged that the movements of the screw which actuates the fiducial hair also actuates a pressure transducer. The signal from this is fed to a meter which gives a direct read-out of the object length. Again the device has to be calibrated initially against the image of a stage micrometer; if many measurements are to be taken, however, then this device increases accuracy by minimizing operator fatigue and consequent errors. A similar device, the Wild 'Censor', is available for a stereo binocular microscope and is shown fitted to the instrument illustrated in Fig. 1–5.

An alternative approach to the problem avoids the use of fiducial hairs to span the object but instead uses an optical device to double the image. The two images (one of which is coloured red, the other green by means of filters) may be moved or 'sheared' relative to each other by means of a micrometer screw. This allows a reading to be obtained firstly when the two images are just touching and secondly when they are in complete coincidence. From the difference, the required size may be calculated. This system is claimed to increase the accuracy of measurement by a factor of ten with respect to the simple micrometer eyepiece.

Measurements of length or diameter enter into almost every field of microscopical work and specific examples are surely unnecessary.

If isolated cells are being examined, e.g. tissue culture cells in a liquid medium or blood cells or spermatozoa in semen, it is often of great importance to know how many cells are present in a given volume of fluid. This can easily be determined by mounting a sample, diluted if necessary, in a special counting chamber called a 'haemocytometer'. This, in its standard form, is basically a microscope slide which has mounted on it a small chamber of known depth, usually 0.1 mm and which is covered by a thick coverslip. The base of the chamber is engraved with a series of squares of known size; the pattern of these varies but often a single square of 3 mm side is subdivided into nine smaller squares each 1 mm across. The centre square of the group is then further subdivided into 400 squares, each of side length 0.05 mm, grouped into twenty-five blocks each containing sixteen of the smaller squares (Fig. 3–7). As the chamber is 0.1 mm deep, the volume of liquid above each of the smallest squares is 0.00025 mm^3. In use the chamber is filled under standardized conditions and the number of cells lying over each of a given number of the smallest squares is counted. Simple arithmetic then enables the total number of suspended cells in 1 mm^3 of the liquid to be calculated. In clinical medicine such counts are routinely carried out on blood samples, in order to ascertain the number of red and white cells per cubic millilitre; as the normal range of values is well established for both males and females, any significant variations may provide valuable diagnostic information for the doctor. In general biological work such cell counts are used to provide information on growth and division rates of cells such as yeasts or bacteria in culture and for many other purposes.

3.5   Stereology

Stereology is the name given to a group of techniques which allow the derivation of three-dimensional structure and numerical parameters from two-dimensional images of sections or projections. Such analyses of tissues must necessarily be based upon several assumptions; among these are requirements that the individual components of interest are fairly numerous in the tissue, that they are easily identifiable in the sections and that they are randomly and irregularly arranged throughout the tissue. If

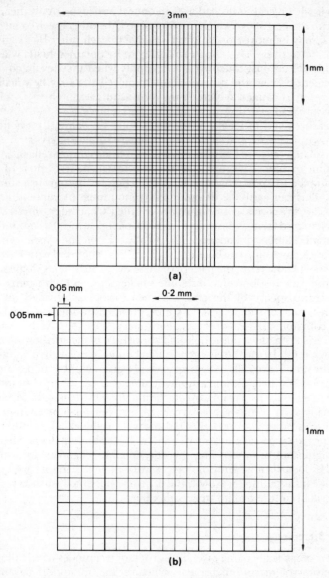

Fig. 3-7 (a) A diagram of a haemocytometer ruling used for counting cells under the microscope. The nine blocks of 1 mm squares can be seen. (b) An enlarged view of the centre block; this is further subdivided into twenty-five 0.2 mm squares each of which is further subdivided into sixteen squares of 0.05 mm side length.

the components are showing a marked order or anisotropy, e.g. as in the parallel arrangement of myofilaments in a muscle fibre, then special, rather complex techniques of analysis must be applied in order to obtain valid results.

The majority of methods used in this field consist of superimposing an image of a suitable test system of points or lines upon the image of the biological tissue to be analysed and simply counting the number of points of the test system which fall on or intersect the component of interest. From the average value of many such counts carried out upon several randomly taken sections through the organ, the required numerical values may be calculated. This use of averages is not a great drawback, as in biology the majority of stereological problems are concerned only with acquiring data related to large populations of cells or organelles which are all identical, or nearly so.

In practice the two most commonly required parameters are the 'volume density' of a component and its 'surface density'. Volume density, represented by the symbol V_V, is defined as that volume of a component contained within a unit volume of cytoplasm or matrix (e.g. the volume of chloroplast material in a unit volume of cell cytoplasm). Surface density (S_V), on the other hand, is the surface area of any component per unit volume; this is often of value in assessing physiological function, e.g. of the alveoli of the lung or of the exchange surface available in the placental villi. Other parameters which can be derived are the numerical density (the number of particles contained within a unit volume of matrix) and the size distribution of a population of spherical objects.

It is common for the test probes of a stereological analysis system to be drawn out on a transparent graticule which is inserted into the eyepiece of the microscope. The image of the test probe points (represented by the two ends of each line) is seen superimposed on the image of the section (Fig. 3–8) and it is then simple to count how many intersections or points lie on the objects of interest. If the problem requires very large numbers of sections to be analysed, it is often a great help to work with projected images so as to minimize fatigue; again with large projects some form of automated data-handling facilities are desirable.

In order to illustrate the principles, let us suppose that a simple two-phase system is being studied. We superimpose our graticule image and count the number of points of the test system which fall upon phase A (say P_A) and the number which fall upon phase B (say P_B); the total number of points counted is thus the sum of the two (which we may represent as P). It is of course necessary to perform a large number of separate counts on different sections of the material in order to obtain results which are accurate and representative of the composition of the tissue as a whole. From the counts the area fraction of the two phases may be calculated. In our hypothetical example, the number of points of the test system falling

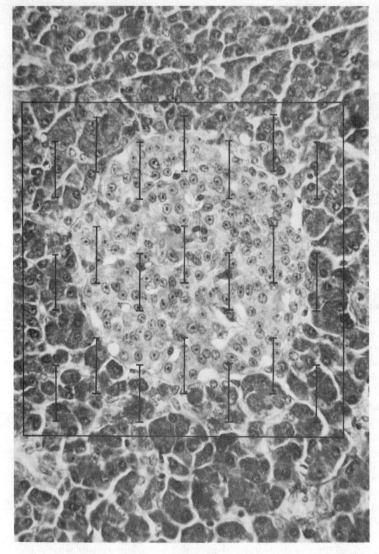

Fig. 3–8 A section of pancreas, showing an islet of Langerhans, with a graticule for stereological measurements superimposed.

on phase A is used to calculate the point fraction of that component from the expression P_A/P. Similarly the point fraction for component B is P_B/P. It can be shown that the point fraction thus obtained for each phase is also equal to the *areas* occupied by the same components. Furthermore, by the application of a principle originally derived in 1847 by the French geologist DeLesse, the area fraction (written A_A) may be shown to be equivalent to the desired volume fraction V_V. These relationships which are fundamental to stereological analysis, may thus be written

$$P_P = A_A = V_V.$$

Full details of the mathematical derivation of these relationships and of others equally valuable to the stereologist (for example those for deriving the surface density of components) may be found in the works listed in the bibliography. It should again be emphasized that stereological relationships and techniques are valid only for situations in which the limitations of proper sampling are observed. The methods (which must deal with large numbers of structures) produce only average values for the parameters characterizing those structures. Similarly, because the process evaluates these parameters from random sections, the actual process of sectioning allows only a restricted sample from the organ to be analysed and there is therefore always the necessity to extrapolate from the data.

In recent years the techniques of stereology have been applied to numerous biological problems but this field of research is certain to increase in importance as the techniques become more familiar to workers. Dunnill and his co-workers at the Radcliffe Infirmary, Oxford, have used this approach to study the composition of human vertebrae under normal and pathological situations. They carried out a quantitative analysis of bony trabeculae, haemopoetic bone marrow and fatty bone marrow on the lumbar vertebrae from differing age groups and on vertebrae from patients suffering from clinically-demonstrable osteoporosis. It was shown by their study that although the total vertebral volume increases with age, the proportion of the vertebrae occupied by bone remains constant from childhood to the third decade of life, after which there is a general although variable decline with increasing age. The most striking changes, however, occur in the bone marrow; throughout life there is a general decline in the amount of haemopoetic bone marrow in the vertebrae so that the percentage volume of this component in the eighth decade is only approximately half that present in childhood. At the same time there is a corresponding increase in the percentage volume of fatty bone marrow. The cases of osteoporosis which they studied suggested that there was a significant decrease in the percentage volume occupied by the bony trabeculae although because of the small numbers examined considerable overlap between osteoporotic and normal bone was recorded. Such studies linking the biological and clinical fields are now beginning to yield very valuable data. Similar examples in which stereological techniques have been applied are in studies of changes in the volume of mucous glands in the trachea and bronchi of normal and chronic bronchitic patients (which showed that in the latter case there is always a considerable increase above normal values) and in studies of the surface area of the villi in the placenta in normal and abnormal situations.

Similar studies may be carried out on single cells and it is now common for point-counting methods to be used at the electron microscopical level to study the various intracellular organelles such as michondria.

The techniques of morphometric analysis take microscopical observations well beyond the stage that mere structural observations could hope to achieve; not only can we now study the shape and location of cells and organs, but also we can reveal hitherto unsuspected relationships between such cells and organs and show up variations in them which are dependent upon changes in the physiological state of the animal.

3.6   Automatic methods of image analysis

We have seen in the previous section how quantitative data may be obtained from the microscopical image by the application of test probes and point-counting techniques. Although such methods can yield valuable information, they are limited in their application by the amount of labour involved in order to produce statistically-significant results. This restriction has led to considerable research in an effort to automate such techniques for image analysis.

The first major advances in this field were the methods of microspectrophotometry developed from 1936 onwards by Caspersson and his associates. He was primarily concerned to measure the absorption of ultra-violet light of 260 nm wavelength both at single points and along line scans of cells in order to locate and quantify the nucleic acids present in cells. The apparatus required for this type of analysis may range from the very simple to the most complex; essentially, however, all systems follow the same pattern (Fig. 3–9). A light source with an emission spectrum rich in the required wavelengths is used and the light passed through a suitable monochromator with a slit to isolate the desired band of wavelengths. The microscope is provided with a high quality aplanatic condenser, limited, however, to a numerical aperture of 0.3–0.4 in order to ensure that no errors are introduced by extremely oblique rays passing through the specimen. These latter would of course pass through a much greater thickness of tissue than the more central rays and therefore suffer a greater degree of absorption. Microspectrophotometry should be performed with immersion lenses of

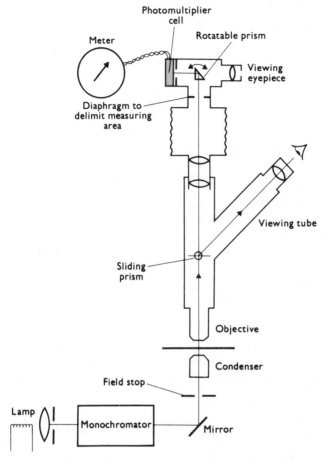

Fig. 3–9 A diagram of the component parts of a simple direct-reading microspectrophotometer, according to the design of Ruthmann.

high quality, although if suitable reflecting or mirror objectives are available these are ideal as they are inherently free from chromatic aberration and have a focal length which is the same at all wavelengths. The light transmitted through any point in the cell under examination is allowed to fall on to a photometer, usually of the highly sensitive photomultiplier variety, fitted with diaphragms to delimit accurately the measuring area. Photocurrents induced in the photomultiplier are amplified and read off on some form of galvanometer. In use, a reading of the photocurrent (say I_O) is taken at some point free of absorbing material to serve as a reference setting; the specimen is then introduced into the beam path and a new reading taken (say I_s). From the Beer-Lambert law of light absorption, the extinction E of the measured area is given by the expression

$$E = \frac{\log I_o}{\log I_s}$$

The value E is in fact the product of C, the concentration of the chromophore, d, the thickness of the absorbing layer and k the absorption coefficient. This latter is a function of the wavelength of measurement and has its maximum value at the absorption maximum of the chromophore. Although the absolute amounts of stained substance are not easily determined with accuracy (because of uncertainty as to the exact value of k) relative concentrations may easily be found: as if in two measurements of extinction $E_1 = kC_1d$ and $E_2 = kC_2d$ and if both d and k are constant, then the ratio of the two concentrations C_1/C_2 is given by the ratio E_1/E_2.

A refinement of the simple type of direct reading microspectrophotometer described above is an arrangement for the measuring spot of light to be scanned over the whole area of the specimen. Integrated measurements thus obtained avoid the distributional errors which are unavoidable with a direct reading instrument. Automatic scanning photometers usually employ either a mechanical stage scan to move the specimen relative to the beam of light or some system of apertures in rotating discs or mirror sectors to move the light beam over the specimen. From such scanning instruments a complete picture of the absorption, transmission and extinction characteristics of the whole specimen may be obtained in a matter of minutes.

The techniques of microspectrophotometry proved to be of great value in cytological studies of nucleic acids. In particular, such measurements of nuclei stained by the Feulgen method (which is specific for deoxyribonucleic acid, DNA) have played a major role in establishing the constancy of the amount of DNA in the genome. Recent improvements to the techniques have even allowed the accurate measurement of the relative DNA content of single bands in the polytene chromosomes found in the Dipteran salivary glands. A further field in which microspectrophotometric measurements have been of value is in showing that in many cancer cells the nucleic acid content differs markedly from that of normal cells.

A different approach to the problems of automating quantitative microscopy was tried by Roberts and Young in 1951. They used a combination of a television cathode-ray tube to produce a scanning spot of light that was passed into the microscope through the optical system but in the reverse direction, i.e. through the eyepiece, objective, specimen and condenser in that order. This meant that the specimen was scanned by a spot of light much reduced in size and hence much smaller than the particles in the field of view being analysed. The spot of light finally affected a photo cell, the pulses from which were amplified and used to modulate a display cathode ray tube operated from the same time base as the scanning spot, so producing an image of the specimen. For counting and measuring purposes a one-line memory system was arranged so that a count pulse was obtained only if the spot was not obscured at the corresponding place on the previous scan line. This system was used for counting the numbers of red blood cells, dust particles and nerve cells in a field of view. Interesting results were obtained but many problems were encountered and further developments in electronic methods of image analysis did not take place until the middle of the 1960's when solid-state circuitry and integrated circuits made the complicated electronic processing techniques into a practical possibility.

Several commercial image analysing microscopes are now available, some based on an optical scanning principle (e.g. the Vickers M85 and M86 scanning interferometer and microdensitometer) whilst others (e.g. the Imanco Quantimet 720) are basically television systems based on the image-plane scan afforded by a plumbicon or vidicon television tube.

The Vickers M86 is a combined integrating interferometer and microdensitometer which has the facility for measurement of integrated optical densities on specimen areas down to 0.3 μm square, at all wavelengths between 400 and 700 nm. In addition it can be arranged to provide a measurement of optical path difference in order to obtain the dry mass of the specimen (see section 3.2). The instrument itself is rather larger than a conventional research microscope, but it will stand conveniently on a laboratory bench (Fig. 3–10).

One present topical use of this instrument in biology is for the measurement of the levels of trophic hormones, such as adrenocorticotrophic hormone (ACTH) in the bloodstream. The method, developed in the Kennedy Institute of Rheumatology in London, has been further refined by workers in the Chemical Pathology department of St. Bartholomew's Hospital. In principle, the target organ for the hormone (the adrenal gland in the case of ACTH) is removed from an animal and cultured *in vitro* for a time to ensure that all former hormonal influences from the original animal are no longer operative. Segments of the target organ are then exposed to accurately known graded concentrations of the hormone whilst at the same time further segments of target organ are exposed for the same length of time to dilutions of the blood plasma which contains the unknown quantity of hormone to be assayed. After a suitable time the organ segments are sectioned on a cryostat and the resulting thin sections are separately treated with a cytochemical reagent which produces a coloured end-product in the tissues.

The intensity of this colour depends upon the concentration of the

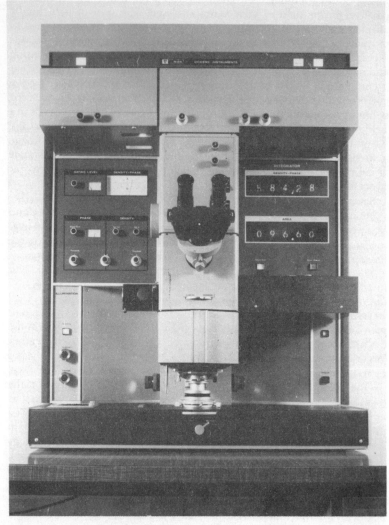

Fig. 3–10 The Vickers M86 scanning microdensitometer.

hormone in the medium in which the target organ was incubated. The scanning microdensitometer is then used to measure the intensity of the staining reaction in each section by scanning integrating microdensitometry; as some of the sections were incubated in known concentrations of hormone these may be used to construct a calibration graph from which it is a simple matter to read off the concentrations in the experimental specimens. The assays are rapidly and easily carried out with such an automatic instrument, a very necessary condition in any technique intended for use as a routine assay. Reproducibility is good (better than 1%); from the calibration graph of integrated optical density plotted against known concentrations of hormone, the hormone concentration responsible for producing any optical density encountered in the experimental material may be determined. So high is the sensitivity of this modern microscopical method of assay that 5 femtograms (5×10^{-15}g) of ACTH per ml. of plasma may be measured, an increase of 500–1000 times in sensitivity when compared with the conventional radio-immunoassay methods at present in routine use. This means that only very small quantities of plasma are needed for an assay with the microdensitometer, so making it a very useful tool when investigating abnormal hormone levels in foetal or neonatal animals. The use of this technique may well prove of tremendous value in experimental endocrinology.

Another approach to automating data acquisition from the microscope image is represented by the Quantimet Image Analysing Computer or QTM 720 for short. This uses a television scanning system linked to a central processor unit together with various output peripherals for the handling of the large amounts of numerical data so obtained; a large QTM 720 system is shown in Fig. 3–11. The input image may be provided from any form of microscope, either optical or electron, or (by means of an epidiascope attachment) from a photomicrograph or drawing. The image is scanned by a vidicon or a plumbicon camera, the signal from which is passed to the computer (located in the central processor unit). From the computer it is possible to derive areas, perimeters, intercept values (a measure of the number of times the scan line intersects the object, i.e. the vertical height) and counts of the number of detected features per field. A display TV monitor tube is provided which allows the operator to monitor not only the input signal but also every measurement operation which takes place. The numerical results from the QTM 720 may be displayed in digital form on the top of the monitor screen, fed on to a teletype or data punch or, alternatively, be led directly into a desktop programmable-calculator for further processing. All the measuring sequences and switching operations can be controlled automatically.

Recent additions to the system include a densitometer and a series of pattern-recognition modules which allow features to be classified by means of a wide variety of size, shape and density criteria. For example, a field of view containing, say, long thin fibres and round cell nuclei of equal optical density may be analysed because the pattern recognition modules compute a value for the parameter

$$\frac{\text{Area}}{(\text{Perimeter})^2}$$

this is an orientation-independent descriptive feature which will differ markedly for the two shapes quoted above. Each may be then measured in turn by altering the preset values on the modules.

Fig. 3–11   A large QTM 720 image analysing computer. From left to right: the Hewlett Packard 9830 calculator; the microscope input peripheral; the display and control modules.

Such instruments were originally designed for use in the field of materials science, but now they are rapidly becoming invaluable to the life sciences. Interesting information may be gained about the nucleic acid content of isolated nuclei (for example in a smear of cells obtained from the cervix of the uterus and stained with the Feulgen technique) in very little time as compared with the traditional methods of densitometry. Normal cervical cells show a distribution of optical densities very closely clustered about the mode which represents the 2c value (Fig. 3–12) whereas in cases of abnormality (possibly associated with the development of an overt carcinoma) there is a much greater spread of values with many nuclei having much more DNA. The histogram also shows an obvious tendency to the development of polyploid and aneuploid strains of cells. With the facilities for complex measurements available on the QTM 720 it is possible to obtain for each individual nucleus information not only about its optical density but also values for its area, perimeter and other features. From these it is possible to construct scatter diagrams in which optical density, say, is plotted against area, for each nucleus in a sample. When this is done (Fig. 3–13) and the

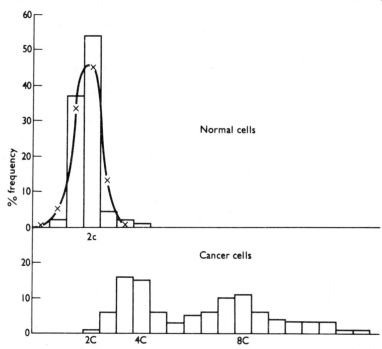

Fig. 3–12 Histograms of the distribution of optical densities in smears from normal and abnormal cervices. The data were obtained with the QTM 720 image analysing computer. Note the much greater spread and the aneuploidy shown by the abnormal specimen and the close correspondence to the normal distribution indicated by the curve superimposed on the upper histogram.

regression line of area upon optical density is drawn for each group of cells, it is seen that the normal differs markedly from the abnormal, not only in the position of the cluster of points but also in the slope of the regression line. This suggests that the increase in area shown by the abnormal nuclei is due not only to their increased content of DNA noted above, but also to other factors which have not yet been identified. Use of the calculator 'on-line' to the QTM 720 together with the ability to set different threshold levels allows many further features to be derived. If, for example, sections are prepared of blood vessels in which the lumen has been filled up by the injection of an opaque substance before or just at death, then this may be detected on one channel of the instrument whilst the substance of the vessel wall (which has a different optical density) may be detected on a second channel. It is thus possible to obtain information which will allow the calculation of the area of the lumen at the level of the section, the mean thickness of the vessel wall at that level and to derive

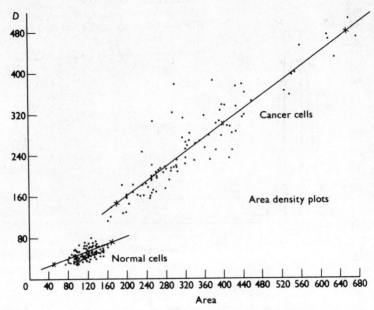

Fig. 3–13   A scatter diagram constructed from QTM 720 data of the optical densities plotted against areas for normal and abnormal nuclei stained by the Feulgen technique. The regression lines of area/density have been added. D on the Y axis represents integrated optical density (in arbitrary machine units); the area values are given in 'picture points', the value of which depends upon the optical magnification used on the microscope.

expressions which serve as 'shape factors' for both lumen and outer surface of the vessel. All of these may be measured and calculated and printed out within two seconds; allowing time to change the specimen it is thus possible to measure at least 120 sections per hour. In addition, at the end of each series of measurements it is easy to obtain mean values together with the standard statistical parameters such as standard deviation, standard error of the mean, regressions and correlation coefficients together with a graphical expression of the accumulated data, all at the touch of a button.

The pattern-recognition modules are proving extremely useful to the biologist as most of the features of interest in microscopical specimens are of complex shapes. Often in the measurements of cervical cells quoted above it was found that the round or oval profiles of the cells of interest were mingled with the multi-lobed profiles of contaminant leucocytes. By using the form factor

$$\frac{\text{Area}}{(\text{Perimeter})^2}$$

already mentioned it proved possible to programme the QTM 720 to ignore all the contaminating white blood cells on the smear and to measure only the cervical cells.

New modules are continually being added to the QTM 720 system; the latest of these, the 'image editor', consists of an interactive light pen which allows the operator to amend the displayed image on the screen, in order to improve faulty detection of features of interest, to reject spurious features or to separate features of interest which are touching and which otherwise the machine would treat as a single feature.

This module, by allowing the shape and pattern recognition capabilities of the human brain to be added to the measuring capabilities of the computer has greatly simplified the application of image analysis techniques in biology.

At present the QTM 720 is a newcomer to biological quantitative microscopy. The machine is obviously a very powerful tool in research, although there are still many problems in its application to be overcome; often biological specimens do not possess sufficient contrast to enable them to be detected easily; alternatively, their shapes may be so complex that suitable descriptors have not yet been worked out. Once these initial difficulties have been overcome, which is surely only a matter of time, then the speed and versatility of the QTM 720 (and similar instruments produced by other manufacturers) will undoubtedly ensure the rapid advance of this new field of automated microscopical image analysis.

Appendix: Practical Notes on the use of the Microscope

Most scientific instruments, if used incorrectly, will provide nonsensical information; unfortunately this is not true of the microscope, which provides an image (of sorts) even when it is poorly adjusted or operated. Correct use of the microscope is easy, and the improvement in image quality is then so marked that every user should endeavour to adjust the microscope properly every time it is used.

In order to obtain the best possible results and image quality from any given instrument make sure that the condenser, eyepiece and objective lenses are clean. Lens tissues are ideal for gentle cleaning operations but 'Kleenex' tissues make an acceptable substitute. If the front lens of the objective is contaminated, the resolution and contrast of the image suffer very severely. Grease, finger marks and the occasional accidental contamination with mounting medium or immersion oil may be removed by wiping with lens tissue moistened with xylene (*never* alcohol of any strength). Dust particles on the eyepiece or condenser lenses may be troublesome, and are often difficult to locate: if the specks rotate in the field of view when the eyepiece is rotated then they must be on either the field or eye lens of the ocular. It is usually permissible to unscrew these lenses and clean them with tissues. Often a blower as used for cleaning camera lenses is a help, as the jet of air may be sufficient to dislodge the dust. Dust on the condenser lenses is often revealed as this unit is racked up and down during its focusing. The condenser should be gently removed from its mounting and cleaned with a blower and/or the gentle use of lens tissue.

Under no circumstances should a microscope objective be separated into its component parts. Cleaning should be restricted to wiping the front element as mentioned above and to gentle use of the blower to remove any settled dust from the upper surface of the rear element.

In order to minimize dust problems, the microscope should be covered with a polythene dust cover when not in use (or, of course, replaced in its proper case) and the tube should never be left without an eyepiece or a blanking plug fitted in the upper end.

Setting up a microscope (using an external lamp) to obtain correct source-focused illumination

Use the ×10 objective lens and proceed as follows.

(1) Place a suitable stained slide on the stage of the microscope and a lamp about 15–20 cm away from the instrument and square to it. The lamp should

contain an opal bulb and have a circular field stop fitted, but if these are not available a laboratory lamp may be used to illuminate tracing paper or finely ground glass fixed to one side of a hole cut in a piece of blackened cardboard. The illuminated area then may be treated as a secondary light source.

(2) Focus the slide and manipulate the mirror to centre the illumination.

(3) Focus the microscope condenser. If a medium-sized field stop is used, an out-of-focus image of it may be seen in the field of view. Adjust the position of the microscope condenser by means of its focusing mechanism until the image of the periphery of the field stop is visible in sharp focus at the same time as the image of the object on the microscope stage. Note: colour fringes and ghost images of the edge of the field stop may be seen. These are due to imperfections in the corrections of the condenser and to multiple reflections from the glass of the mirror; they may be ignored. Alternatively, if the image of the only field stop available more than fills the field of view of the microscope, a pencil point or mounted needle may be positioned in the plane of the field stop opening and its image focused by the condenser movements in the same way. The focusing of the condenser needs repeating only when slides of widely differing thickness are used.

(4) Change to the 4 mm (x 40) objective.

(5) Adjust the aperture of the iris diaphragm to suit the numerical aperture of the 4 mm lens. This is done by removing the eyepiece and looking directly at the brightly illuminated circle of the back of the objective lens. As the iris diaphragm is closed, the image of its edge will be seen to encroach on the illuminated area. Close the diaphragm until the diameter of the illuminated portion of the objective occupies about three-quarters of its whole diameter. This adjustment, although carried out with the x 40 lens, will also serve for the x 10 lens. It is not possible to detect any difference in the image quality if the aperture is further reduced (in the same way) to the correct value for the x 10 lens, and a single setting for the x 40 lens saves time and trouble.

(6) Replace the eyepiece. The microscope is now in correct adjustment and is ready for use.

If the light is too bright, its intensity should be moderated by the use of suitable neutral density filters placed at any convenient point in the light path.

Setting up to obtain correct Köhler illumination with an external light source
This type of illumination is especially suited for phase-contrast, polarized

light and photomicrography. It is essential if any blue-light fluorescence is to be attempted. The microscope lamp housing must possess a well-corrected condenser lens and it is desirable for it to have an iris diaphragm which will act as a field stop.

(1) Place a stained slide on the microscope stage and focus with the low power lens. Align the microscope lamp about 20–25 cm in front of the microscope mirror.

(2) Close the lamp field stop (or substitute smaller diaphragms) until it is visible in the field of view of the microscope. It will be necessary to focus this image with the microscope condenser lens. Centre the image of the field stop with the mirror adjustments.

(3) Close the condenser iris diaphragm fully and focus an image of the lamp filament on to it. Use the *lamp* condenser for this purpose. The image of the lamp filament must be central with respect to the substage iris diaphragm and this may be achieved by small movements of the lamp (as the mirror has already been adjusted to give axial illumination). It may be necessary to make a final slight adjustment of the mirror position if the lamp is moved appreciably. Note: a small mirror fixed into a piece of Plasticine and placed on the bench allows the image of the lamp filament on the substage diaphragm to be observed in comfort. The size of the image should just fill the aperture of the substage condenser for optimum results. If this is not attainable without moving the lamp further away, then the lamp condenser should be replaced by one of shorter focal length.

(4) Open the condenser iris diaphragm fully; open the field stop until the illuminated area just occupies the field of view; remove the eyepiece and adjust the working aperture of the condenser as described above for source-focused illumination, again using the 4 mm lens.

Setting up of Köhler illumination with a microscope having a built-in lamp follows very closely the principles laid down above, but because of the widely differing adjustments provided by the various makers it is recommended that the instruction book for the microscope should be followed.

Remember that the iris diaphragm serves to control the numerical aperture of the objective lens. It does *not* control the intensity of the illumination, and should never be used for this purpose. With a low-voltage lamp, there is nearly always a rheostat for adjusting the brightness but if not (or if the colour temperature of the light is important, as in photomicrography) then graded density filters must be used.

Bibliography

(a) General

BARRON, A. L. E. (1965). *Using the Microscope*. Chapman & Hall Ltd. London.
COSSLETT, V. E. (1966). *Modern Microscopy*. Bell. London.
WHITE, G. W. (1966). *Introduction to Microscopy*. Butterworth & Co. (Publishers) Ltd., London.

Instructions on the construction of dark ground stops are given in *Additional Notes on the use of the Microscope* (S. Bradbury) published by the Royal Microscopical Society, Oxford.

(b) Historical

BRADBURY, S. (1967). *The Evolution of the Microscope*. Pergamon, Oxford.

(c) Phase contrast, modulation contrast and interference microscopy

BESSIS, M. (1973). *Living Blood Cells and their Ultrastructure*. Springer Verlag, New York.
HOFFMAN, R. and GROSS, L. (1975). Modulation Contrast Microscope. *Applied Optics*, 14, 1169–1176.
HOFFMAN, R. and GROSS, L. (1975). The Modulation Contrast Microscope. *Nature*, 254, 586–588.
ROSE, G. G. Ed. (1963). *Cinemicrography in Cell Biology*. Academic Press, New York and London.
ROSS, K. F. A. (1967). *Phase Contrast and Interference Microscopy for Cell Biologists*. Edward Arnold (Publishers) Ltd., London.

(d) Photomicrography

WALKER, M. I. (1971). *Amateur Photomicrography*. Focal Press, Ltd., London.

(e) Polarizing microscopy

HALLIMOND, A. F. (1970). *The Polarizing Microscope*. Vickers Instruments, Yorkshire.
RUCH, F. (1966). Birefringence and Dichroism of Cells and Tissue in *Physical Techniques in Biological Research*, Vol. IIIA, 57–87. Academic Press, London and New York.

(f) Stereology

DUNNILL, M. S., ANDERSON, J. A. and WHITEHEAD, R. (1967). Quantitative Histological Studies on Age Changes in Bone. *J. Path. Bact.*, 94, No. 2, 275–91.

ELIAS, H., HENNIG, A. and SCHWARTZ, D. (1971). Stereology—Applications to Biological Research. *Physiol. Rev.*, **51**, 158–200.

WEIBEL, E. R. and ELIAS, H. Eds. (1967). *Quantitative Methods in Morphology*. Springer Verlag, New York.

(g) Fluorescence microscopy

CASPERSSON, T., LINDSTEN, J., LOMAKKA, G., MØLLER, A. and ZECK, L. (1972). The Use of Fluorescence Techniques for the Recognition of Mammalian Chromosomes and Chromosome Regions. *Int. Rev. Exp. Path.*, **11**, 1–72.

YOUNG, R., (1961). Principles and Techniques of Fluorescence Microscopy. *Quart. J. micr. Sci.*, **102**, 419–49.

(h) Methods of automatic image analysis

FISHER, C. (1971). The New Quantimet 720. *The Microscope*, **19**, 1–20.